Science Experiments
With Water

SCIENCE

Illustrated by
JOHN J. FLOHERTY, JR.

EXPERIMENTS
WITH WATER

by SAM ROSENFELD

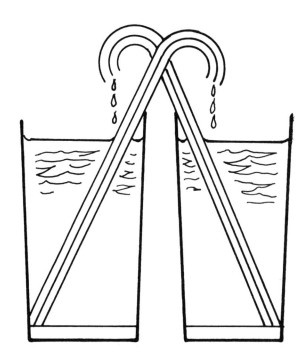

HARVEY HOUSE, INC. • *Publishers*
Irvington-on-Hudson • New York

To my good friends, the Langs —
Sylvia, Raymond, Mana, Pat
and Andrew

HARVEY HOUSE, INC. • *Publishers*
Irvington-on-Hudson • New York

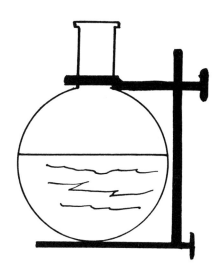

CONTENTS

14,710.

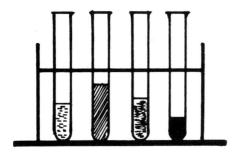

PREFACE

One of the most interesting developments in the field of education is step-by-step instruction through experiment and discussion. The technique, as applied in this book, arranges a body of knowledge into a series of experiments and discussions, followed by questions and answers of progressive difficulty.

An important feature of this book is the ease with which the young scientist can verify the accuracy of his work before proceeding to more difficult material. The series of questions at the end of each chapter reinforce what he has already understood and emphasize the most important points. An incorrect answer allows the reader to review the experiment and then the discussion, to find what he overlooked or failed to understand. Thus, analysis and research are encouraged.

It is the author's hope that this book will open the door to the wonderful world of science where today's knowledge becomes tomorrow's frontier.

(*Courtesy Fisher Scientific, Inc.*)

10

FAMOUS SCIENTISTS

(*Wide World Photos Inc.*)

SIR ISAAC NEWTON (1642-1727), English philosopher and mathematician, is considered one of the greatest scientists of all time. He conceived the law of gravitation and is credited with the invention of differential and integral calculus. Besides studying light and color, he constructed the reflecting telescope. Newton was appointed master of the mint in 1669 and was knighted in 1705.

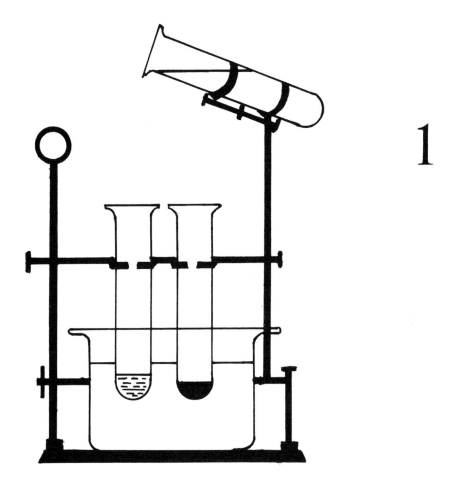

1

IS WATER REALLY HEAVY?

All substances are attracted to the earth. This is so because of a force called gravity. The size of the force for a particular object is called its weight, and the more there is of that substance, the more it weighs. Although this fact seems obvious, let us perform the following simple experiment with water and see if it is really so.

First, lift a basin or pail of water. It will, of course, be heavy. Next, place your hand in the water near the top and then at the bottom. Do you feel a greater weight of water on your hand when it is at the bottom? The answer should be "no." This is quite puzzling, for if water has weight, you should feel the weight of the water on your hand when you hold it near the bottom of the pail.

If you had performed the same experiment using a column of wooden blocks instead of water, without doubt you would have felt more weight if your hand were under the lowest block than if it were under the highest.

In this experiment you will discover what actually determines the weight or pressure of water at a particular point. Later experiments will explore why no weight was felt when you placed your hand inside the pail.

MATERIALS: Large standard juice can, 7 inches high; narrow frozen juice can 7 inches high; water; nail.

METHOD: Part I — With a hammer and nail, punch a hole about one inch from the top of the large juice can. Place another hole one inch from the bottom of the can and another midway between the two holes (Fig. 1–1a). Perform the next part of the experiment over a sink or basin. Fill the can with water and observe the streams of water. They should appear as in Figure 1–1b.

Part II — Punch holes in the narrower frozen juice can as in Part I and fill with water. Observe the stream of water from

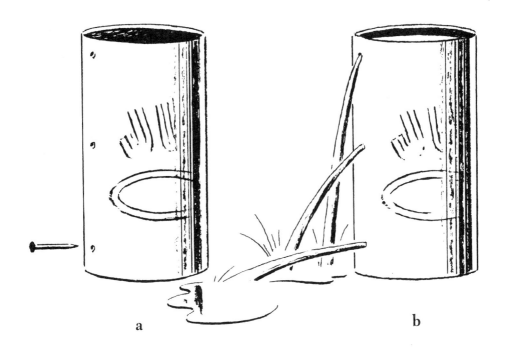

What causes the water to spurt out furthest at the lowest opening?

Figure 1–1

each opening. Perform the experiment with both cans at the same time and compare the lengths of the streams of water.

***

DISCUSSION: The weight of the water causes it to leave forcibly through each hole in the can. Since the water's weight is least at the topmost opening, the stream does not go very far. At the lowest opening, the water will spurt forth the greatest distance. The experiment in Part II proved that the greater amount of water in the wider can had no effect on the length of the stream. Instead, the *height* of the water determined how far the stream would go. The weight, as determined by the height, is called water pressure.

Water pressure is one of the hazards of skin diving. As a diver sinks deeper and deeper into the water, the pressure on his body steadily increases. The parts of his body most sensitive to pressure are his eardrums. If a diver goes down too quickly, his eardrums may break, with the possibility of permanent damage to his hearing.

Now that we have demonstrated that water produces pressure, it should be even more puzzling that no pressure was felt on your hand when you placed it under water during the first part of the experiment. That question will be answered in the next experiment.

SELF-TEST
ANSWERS ON PAGE 171

1. What causes the streams of water to leave forcibly through each hole in the can?

2. At what part of the can is the least weight of water?

3. At which opening in the can will water spurt out the greatest distance?

4. What determined the extent to which a stream of water was forced out of an opening?

5. In this experiment, what caused water pressure?

6. What parts of a diver's body are most sensitive to water pressure?

BLAISE PASCAL (1623-1662), French, showed his genius when, at the age of sixteen, he wrote a scientific paper about mathematics. He discovered what is now known as Pascal's Law: pressure applied to a liquid is spread equally in all directions within the liquid. His study of the atmosphere led him to the discovery that the pressure of air decreases as we travel up a mountain.

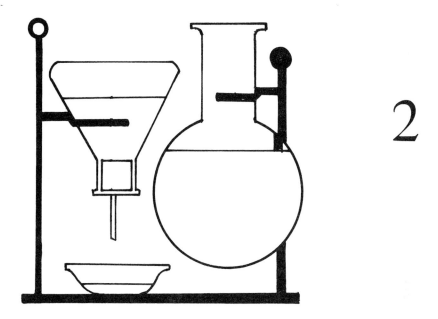

HOW DOES WATER MULTIPLY PRESSURE?

The previous experiment demonstrated that the height of water, and not the amount, determined pressure at a particular point. This is a useful property of water for it makes it possible to produce a large amount of pressure with a small amount of force. We might even be able to use this property to help us lift an automobile.

In 1653, Blaise Pascal, a French scientist, discovered that pressure applied to a liquid at one point spreads throughout the liquid. Since it would be somewhat awkward for us to use this property of liquids to lift a car, we can do the next best thing, and use the power of water to lift a friend.

MATERIALS: A willing friend; hot water bottle and a hose

(Photo courtesy General Motors.)

Pascal's principle is used to lift an automobile.

about 6 feet long; funnel; water; wooden board, 6 inches by 10 inches.

METHOD: Part I — Insert the funnel into the hose as illustrated in Figure 2–1a. Place the wooden board on the empty hot water bottle and have someone stand on it. Hold the funnel and hose about five feet above the ground and pour water into it until the funnel is half full.

Though it may appear that your friend's weight will prevent the water from entering the hot water bottle, you will soon discover that it will not only enter the bottle, but it will lift him — or her. Raise and lower the funnel several times. What happens each time?

Part II — You have often heard the expression, "water seeks its own level." This means that water will attempt to flow so that no part of the water is higher than any other part. Demonstrate this by removing the hose from the hot water bottle as in Figure 2–1b. Add water to the funnel until the hose is filled and hold it so that both ends are at the same height. Raise the end opposite the funnel and observe that water enters the funnel; both liquid levels will continue to be equal. Raise the funnel above the level of the other end; water will flow out of the lower end. Why?

✖✖✖

DISCUSSION: Observe that pressure depends on the height of the liquid. In the previous experiment, the stream of water at the lowest opening in the can went furthest. In this experiment, the higher the funnel and hose are held, the more easily a weight is lifted. A column of water 5 feet high and 1 inch square will exert a force of a little over 2 pounds. The pressure is then said to be 2 pounds per square inch.

Pascal discovered three centuries ago (as you will rediscover) that the pressure of a liquid at one point is *spread equally throughout the liquid*. In other words, the wooden board, which has an area of 60 square inches, has a pressure acting on it of over 2 pounds on each square inch of surface in contact with the hot water bottle. This totals over 120 pounds of force and will lift anyone weighing up to that amount.

Pour water into funnel.

Figure 2–1a

In Part II, Figure 2–1b, raising the water level at A increases its pressure, causing it to flow toward B until both levels and pressures are equal. The huge water towers you have undoubtedly seen, furnish water pressure for homes and factories by employing a similar principle.

What happens as one end is raised?

Figure 2–1b

Because of its weight, the water at the top of the tower exerts a tremendous pressure upon the water within the pipes along the ground. This water cannot rise to the level of the water in the tower because there are no pipes leading upward to that height. However, the pressure within the pipes causes the water to spurt out when faucets are opened. This is similar to the experiment on page 14 where the pressure of the water caused it to spurt out of the holes in the juice cans. Additional water is pumped into the storage tank at the top so that there is continuing water pressure for the town or industry (Fig. 2–2).

(Picture of Water Tower, courtesy U.S. Weather Bureau.)

Figure 2–2

At a filling station, oil is used instead of water for lifting a car. Oil reduces friction and will not easily evaporate or corrode metal. Instead of using the weight of a tall column of oil to produce pressure, air is forced against a reservoir of oil by means of a pump (Fig. 2–3). This pressure is transmitted

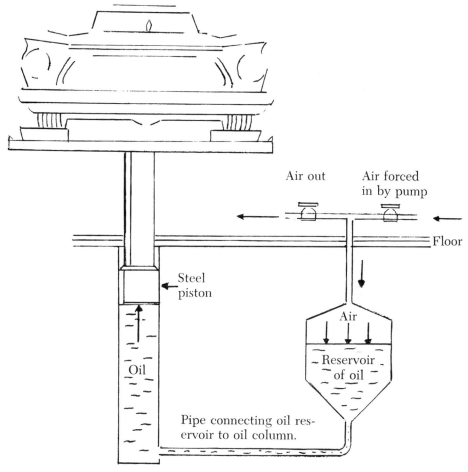

Figure 2–3

(1) Air is forced in through the pipe labeled AIR IN.
(2) The air pushes with great force against the reservoir of oil which is connected by a pipe to the vertical column of oil at the left.
(3) The pressure is transmitted to the oil in the vertical column.
(4) The oil pushes upward against the steel piston, lifting the car.
(5) When air is let out through the AIR OUT pipe, the pressure decreases and the car goes down.

throughout the oil (Pascal's Law — page **21**) and the oil in the vertical column at the left pushes against a steel surface, lifting the car. This is called a hydraulic press.

Now we can answer the question as to why you didn't feel the weight of the water when you placed your hand at the bottom of the pail in the previous experiment. The answer is that since pressure is transmitted in all directions within a liquid, the upward pressure against the bottom of your hand was greater by a small amount (since the water was a bit deeper) than the pressure on top of your hand. As a result you felt no weight of water. If there were a way for you to place your hand flat against the bottom of the pail so that there was absolutely no water between your palm and the bottom of the pail, it would be difficult for you to raise your hand straight up because of the pressure of the water downward.

SELF-TEST
ANSWERS ON PAGE 171

1. What is the name of the French scientist who experimented with liquids?

2. Will the weight of a 120 pound person prevent water from entering the water bottle in this experiment?

3. How does the water pressure distribute itself upon entering the hot water bottle?

4. What happens to water pressure when a column of water is lengthened?

5. What enables a water tower to transmit a great deal of water pressure?

6. How is pressure transmitted in a hydraulic press?

7. Why don't you feel the weight of water when you place your hand at the bottom of a pail of water?

ARCHIMEDES (257-212 B.C.), Greek, is said to have invented the lever, pulleys for lifting heavy weights, and a revolving spiral pump to raise water from the Nile River. He is best remembered for his studies on the buoyancy of water, which enabled him to determine whether or not the crown of King Hiero II of Syracuse was made of pure gold. Archimedes is said to have been killed by the Romans who captured Syracuse.

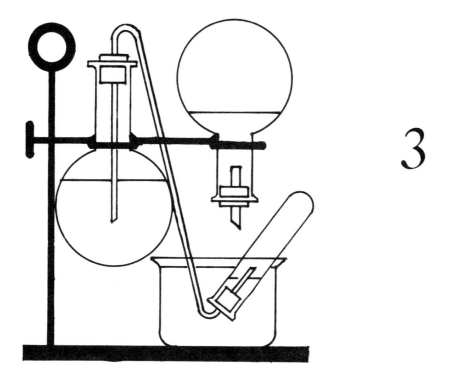

3

HOW DOES A STEEL SHIP FLOAT?

Why does a steel ship float whereas another piece of the same steel will sink? Why does a rubber ball float and why does your own weight seem to decrease as you enter a pool? The answers can be summarized by one word — buoyancy, the ability of a substance to float. In this experiment we will explain its causes and effects.

In 250 B.C., Archimedes, a Greek scientist living in Sicily, was asked by King Hiero II of Syracuse to determine whether a crown made by a certain goldsmith was of gold or of a less valuable metal. The story is told that one day, while in a public bath, Archimedes noticed that the more his body was im-

What happens when water
is added to the floating can?

Figure 3–1

mersed in the water, the higher the surface of the water rose, and the lighter his body appeared to be.

He became so excited that he shouted, "Eureka!" ("I have found it!"), leaped out of his tub and, without bothering to dress, ran all the way home to try the experiment. Before completing the story, let us perform some experiments that will help us observe the laws of buoyancy and enable us to understand what Archimedes discovered.

MATERIALS: Small frozen juice can; pail of water; glass measuring cup; ruler; salt water; stones or lead shot.

METHOD: Part I — Place the can into the pail of water. Fill the glass measuring cup to the mark at the top and add just enough water from the cup to make the can float upright in the pail of water (Fig. 3–1). Note how much water was added from the measuring cup, and record it on a sheet of paper. With the ruler, measure how far the can has sunk into the water and write down the result.

Add water equal to the amount already in the can, and observe what happens. Measure, once more, the depth of the can in the water. Continue adding like amounts of water until the can sinks. Is there any relation between the amount of water you add each time and the extent to which the can sinks?

Part II — Replace the tap water in the pail with salt water and repeat the experiment. If sea water is not available, it may be necessary to sacrifice a box or two of table salt. Add *tap* water to the juice can, as before. Record your results and compare them to those in Part I. Does this explain why it is easier to float or swim in salt water?

Part III — Repeat either or both experiments, adding pebbles or lead shot to the juice can instead of water. Compare these results to the previous results. Try to estimate very roughly how much space the pebbles or lead shot occupied when the can sank as compared to the amount of water that was needed to sink the can.

✖◡✖

DISCUSSION: In Part I of this experiment you will observe that adding tap water to the floating can will cause it to sink deeper into the water. Adding like amounts of water causes it to sink the same amount each time.

A similar result is obtained in Part II. However, the can will not sink as far in the salt water as it will in the tap water. Adding pebbles or lead shot causes the can to sink to the bottom of the pail long before it is filled.

Why did the metal can float? Oddly enough, it was because of the *weight of the water* in the pail. You will remember that pressure in a liquid is transmitted throughout the liquid, and that the deeper you go, the greater will be the pressure. When the can is placed into the water, it pushes aside (displaces) some water. It sinks until the amount of water it pushes aside weighs as much as the can. At that point the water pressure pushing upward on the can equals the weight of the can — and it floats. When water is added, the can sinks deeper because now the amount of water that must be pushed aside has to equal the weight of the can plus the weight of its contents.

When sufficient water is added to the can so that the

weight of water it displaces in the pail is *less* than the weight
of water plus can, it sinks to the bottom. A steel ship floats for
the same reason. The amount of water it displaces actually
weighs as much as the total weight of the ship plus its cargo
and passengers. It is difficult to believe that water is so heavy.
Imagine a box whose dimensions are one foot in every direc-

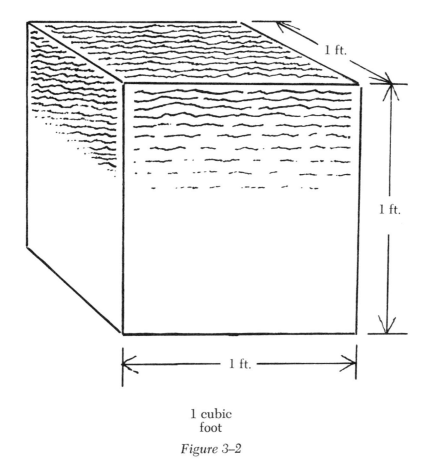

1 ft.

1 ft.

1 ft.

1 cubic
foot

Figure 3–2

tion; this is a cubic foot. When this box is filled with water,
the water will weigh almost 62½ pounds! (Fig. 3–2.)

If the can used in this experiment were flattened or crumpled into a tight ball, its volume — the space it now takes up — would be smaller. It would, therefore, push aside a smaller

(Photo courtesy United States Lines.)
What enables this heavy steel ship to float?

volume of water, whose weight would be *less* than the weight of the can, and it would sink. The reason a steel ship floats is that its metal hull takes up so much space, that when it sinks slightly it displaces a large amount of water.

Why didn't the can sink as far in salt water? Given equal amounts of tap water and salt water, salt water weighs more because of the dissolved salt. When the can displaces the heavier salt water, less salt water is required to equal its weight and the can doesn't sink as far. When pebbles or lead shot were added to the can, they were so much heavier than equal volumes of water that the can had to sink much further to displace an equal weight of water.

Before we can complete Archimedes' story, it will be necessary for us to perform the next experiment.

SELF-TEST
ANSWERS ON PAGE 172

1. What is buoyancy?

2. What is the name of the Greek scientist who discovered the principles of buoyancy?

3. What happens when a small amount of water is added to a floating juice can?

4. Will a floating object sink as deeply in tap water as in salt water?

5. Which is more effective in causing a floating juice can to sink, pebbles or water?

6. What enables an object to float in water?

7. Compare the weight of an object that is able to float with the amount of water it pushes aside.

8. Why will a stone sink?

9. Compare the weight of a steel ship with the volume of water it displaces.

10. How much does a cubic foot of water weigh?

11. Why does an object float more easily in salt water than in tap water?

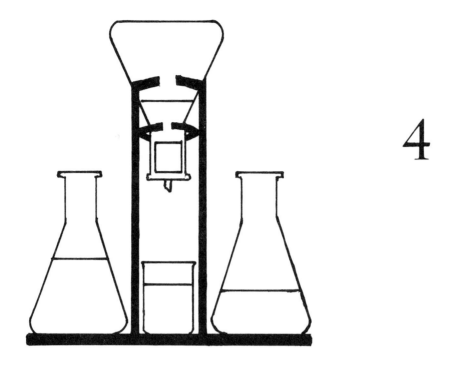

4

LET'S PROVE IT

In the previous experiment, we saw that an object floats because it displaces its own weight in water. This is a logical explanation of the results observed.

But, how do we — you and I — really know that our explanation is correct? We could have offered an equally convincing argument that some objects float because they are repelled by water to a certain extent. We can point to oil and water as an example. Some objects — steel, for instance — do not float because they are attracted to water. However, when such an object is spread out sufficiently (as in a ship), the increased volume of the object causes the attraction to change to a repulsion . . . and on and on and on.

Should we accept an explanation of an event merely because it sounds reasonable? A true scientist does not fully accept any explanation until there is proof. To a scientist, proof generally means measurement, and the more accurate the measurement, the more convincing the proof.

MATERIALS: Standard large juice can, 7 inches tall; small juice can, 3¾ inches tall; rubber or glass tubing, 2 inches long; tap water; salt water; wooden block, 1 inch square and ½ inch thick; cork; postal scales or homemade balance (page 167); candle or sealing wax.

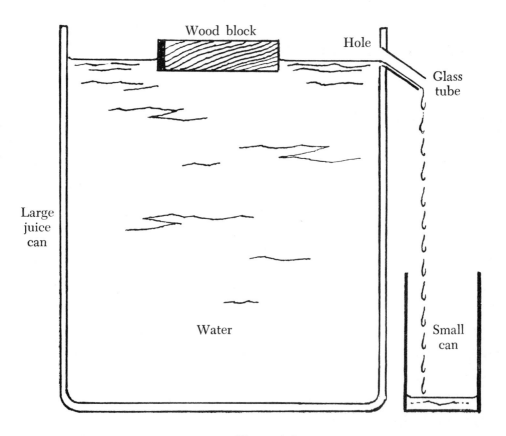

Figure 4–1

JACQUES ALEXANDRE CÉSAR CHARLES (1746-1823), French, invented many scientific instruments; investigated the influence of heat upon the expansion and contraction of gases, and developed what is now known as Charles' Law, which states that when the pressure is not allowed to change, the volume of a gas increases as the temperature increases and decreases as the temperature decreases. In 1785, he was elected to the French Academy.

METHOD: Part I — Drill a hole in the large juice can and insert the small tube at an angle (Fig. 4–1). Affix the tube to the can with wax so that water will not leak out.

Fill the large can with water until it overflows. Weigh the wooden block and the small can separately on an inexpensive postal scale and record the weights. These scales will weigh up to one pound with sufficient accuracy for your experiment, or you may prefer to make a balance. The instructions are given on page 167.

Place the wood into the water as illustrated. The water level will rise and overflow through the small opening into the previously weighed can. Weigh the water plus the can. Determine the weight of the water by subtracting the weight of the empty can. How did the weight of the water compare with that of the wood? How did the volume of the water compare with the size or volume of the block? The volume of a substance is defined as the amount of space it occupies. A small amount of water occupies a small space or volume; a larger amount of water occupies a larger volume. Repeat the experiment using a cork instead of wood.

Part II — Perform the same experiment with a metal ring or stone. How does the weight of the water compare with that of the ring or stone? Does this tell you why they sank and the wood and cork floated?

DISCUSSION: Parts I and II of the experiment demonstrate that the weight of displaced water *equals* the weight of the cork or wood. However, the volume of water is less than either one because water is heavier than wood or cork. A small vol-

(The Bettman Archive, Inc.)

EVANGELISTA TORRICELLI (1608-1647), Italian, is best known for his invention of the mercury barometer which is used to measure air pressure. He also invented a simple microscope and made many improvements in the construction of the telescope. He was an assistant to Galileo, and when the latter died, was appointed in his place as a professor of philosophy and mathematics at Florentine Academy.

ume of water will weigh as much as a slightly larger volume of wood or cork.

41

Part III demonstrates that the weight of the metal or stone is *greater* than the weight of water displaced. Therefore, the metal and stone weigh more than an equal volume of water.

These observations and measurements help us conclude with greater assurance that a floating object displaces an amount of water equal to its own weight. If it is unable to do so, it will sink. Since no exceptions to this have ever been found, this statement is called a *law*.

Archimedes found that equal volumes of different metals

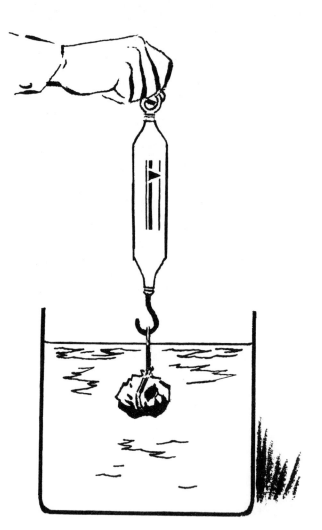

An object appears to weigh less in water because of buoyancy.

Figure 4–2

such as gold, silver, copper, and iron, had different weights. This property of a metal or any substance is called its *density*. Since it was difficult to measure volumes of metals of odd shapes, he conceived the idea of weighing them in water. Their loss in weight as measured by a scale (Fig. 4–2) was due to the buoyancy caused by pushing aside a volume of water equal to the space or volume taken up by the metal, no matter what its size or shape — even if it were shaped like a crown.

By comparing the weight of the metal in air to its apparent loss in weight caused by buoyancy in water, Archimedes was able to obtain a specific value for each metal he tried. This characteristic of a metal is called its *specific gravity*. All he had to do was weigh the crown in air and then in water and compare its specific gravity to the value obtained when he used pure gold. If they were the same, the goldsmith had nothing to worry about. They were not the same, and nobody knows what happened to the goldsmith.

1. What does a scientist require before accepting an explanation of a particular event?

2. What happens to the level of the water in a container when a block of wood is added?

3. A floating object displaces a volume of water equal to its weight. How was this demonstrated?

4. Why doesn't a metal ring float?

5. What is meant by a law of nature?

6. What is the density of a metal?

7. Why does a piece of metal weigh less in water than in air?

8. What is specific gravity?

9. Can a metal be identified by its specific gravity?

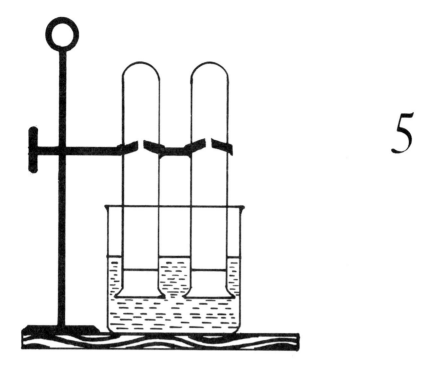

5

THE CARTESIAN DIVER
or
WHAT MAKES A SUBMARINE
RISE AND SINK?

What makes a submarine rise and sink? Is there a way to alter the buoyancy of a body as it floats in water?

In the seventeenth century, René Descartes, a French scientist, studied a toy that changed its buoyancy while in water, so that it rose or sank. The inventor of this toy is unknown. The device was named after Descartes and is called the Cartesian Diver (also known as the Bottle Imp). This is the principle used to control rise and fall in the operation of submarines. The Cartesian Diver can be used to mystify your friends by pretending that it will obey a voice command to go up or down.

MATERIALS: Small pill bottle; wide-mouth jar; rubber membrane (from toy balloon or old bicycle tire); water.

METHOD: Fill the large jar with tap water. Fill the pill bottle about three-quarters full of water. Cover the opening with your thumb and place the bottle, inverted, inside the larger jar.

Stretch the rubber membrane over the top of the jar and keep it in place with a rubber band (Fig. 5–1). When the membrane is pushed downward, the small vial will sink. When the pressure is removed, it will rise. If the vial does not sink upon applying pressure, it contains too much air. If it sinks and does not rise again, it contains too much water. Once the correct amount of water is in the vial, the effect can be repeated indefinitely.

When presenting this as a mystery, keep the top of the bottle slightly above the eye level of your audience. It will prevent them from seeing you apply pressure to the cover. When sold commercially, a figure of a diver is usually substituted for the pill bottle.

❦⊙❦

DISCUSSION: The movements of the Cartesian Diver can readily be explained by the laws of buoyancy. At first, the inverted pill bottle barely floats because its weight plus the weight of water and air inside it displaces an equal weight of

Why does the small vial rise and fall?

Figure 5–1

water in the jar. When pressure is applied to the membrane, it is transmitted equally throughout the liquid, forcing water into the floating vial and causing the air inside to be compressed. The weight of vial, water, and air will now be greater than the weight of the water displaced, and the vial will sink. When pressure is released, the compressed air within the vial pushes out some of the water. The vial becomes lighter and it rises.

RENÉ DESCARTES (1596-1650), French, was a philosopher and mathematician. He always lived near universities and maintained his own science workshop. In science, he relied upon logic and mathematics more than upon experiment. He made many advances in the study of light, algebra, and geometry. He also added to the knowledge of music and psychology.

This can be repeated as often as desired.

A submarine rises or sinks through a similar principle. Valves are opened and water is admitted to the tanks. The weight of submarine plus water becomes greater than the weight of the water displaced, and it sinks. To make the submarine rise, water is forced out of the tanks by compressed air. The weight of the submarine becomes less than the weight of the water it displaces, and it rises.

1. What is a Cartesian Diver?

2. What French scientist described this toy?

3. What is the effect upon the Cartesian Diver when the rubber membrane of the jar is pushed down?

4. Describe what happens when the pressure is removed.

5. How often can this be done?

6. What law describes the movements of the Cartesian Diver?

7. How is water forced intò the vial?

8. Why does the vial sink when the rubber membrane is pressed?

9. What is the effect upon the air within the vial when water is forced in?

10. What happens when pressure on the rubber membrane is released?

11. What causes a submarine to dive?

WHY DOES OIL FLOAT?

Oil appears to be a heavy, sticky fluid that does not flow as easily as water. Yet, when oil and water are brought together, they separate and the oil floats to the top. During World War II, one indication that a submarine had been hit, was a large oil slick that appeared on the surface of the water.

Why does oil float upon water? By this time you can make an intelligent guess; probably because of the lighter weight of oil. It is important, therefore, to remember that a fat, oil, or grease fire should never be fought with water for it will cause the fire to spread. We will observe in this experiment that there are liquids heavier than water and we can predict that they will sink when placed in water — probably.

MATERIALS: Small drinking glass; machine or olive oil; Carbona (cleaning fluid); milk; rubbing alcohol; postal scales or homemade balance, page 167.

METHOD: Part I — Weigh the glass and record the weight. The same glass will be used in each part to enable us to compare equal volumes.

Fill the glass with water completely to the top, and weigh. Subtract the weight of the glass from the weight of the water and glass; this will give you the weight of water alone. Dry and clean the glass for the next part of the experiment.

Part II — Fill the glass to the top with oil, and weigh. Subtract the weight of the glass. How does the weight of the oil compare with that of water? Add some oil to a glass of water. Do your experimental results explain why oil floats on water? Compare this to the reason that a cork floats.

Part III — Fill the weighed glass with Carbona cleaning fluid. Weigh and record. How does its weight compare with that of water? What do you suppose will happen when you pour some of it into a glass of water? Try it.

Part IV — Fill the glass with milk and weigh. How does it compare with water? Predict what will happen when you pour some of it into a glass of water.

Part V — Repeat the experiment with rubbing alcohol. What will happen when you pour it into water? Here is a scientific warning — your prediction may be wrong.

Louis Pasteur (1822-1895), French, proved that fermentation (which produced alcohol) and souring were caused by microscopic living things, which we now call germs; discovered that these germs could be destroyed by heat, thus leading to the pasteurization of milk and to the discovery that most diseases are caused by germs; developed a successful treatment for hydrophobia; member of the Legion of Honor and the French Academy of Sciences.

DISCUSSION: Your experiment should indicate that a volume of oil will weigh less than an equal volume of water. This comparison is called the specific gravity of oil. Compare this with the specific gravity of metals as studied by Archimedes on page 43.

Since the specific gravity of oil is less than water, it will float; because of this, water will not put out an oil fire. Instead, the burning oil will float on top of the water and spread. You can throw sand, table salt, or baking soda on the flames; also, a damp towel spread over the fire will cool and smother it, but be sure that you have wrung out as much water as possible.

The Carbona — also called carbon tetrachloride — is heavier than water and will sink to the bottom. You can observe two distinct layers of clear liquid. Stir the liquids rapidly with a spoon. When you stop, they will immediately separate into two layers.

The milk weighs slightly more than water because of dissolved materials, but your balance may not be sufficiently accurate to detect the difference. When the milk is poured into water, it spreads evenly to form a cloudy mixture since milk is almost entirely water. The cloudiness is caused by tiny droplets of cream which do not settle or rise. This will be discussed in greater detail in a later section.

You will discover that the rubbing alcohol is lighter than water, and should float. However, another factor enters — as often occurs in science. Instead of floating, the alcohol and water dissolve in each other to form one solution which is heavier than alcohol and lighter than water.

SELF-TEST
ANSWERS ON PAGE 173

1. Which flows more easily, oil or water?

2. Why shouldn't an oil fire be fought with water?

3. Which is heavier, oil or water?

4. What happens when water and carbon tetrachloride are mixed together?

5. What happens when oil and water are mixed together?

6. How does the weight of one quart of Carbona compare with the weight of one quart of water?

7. Which weighs more, one quart of milk or one quart of water?

8. What is meant by the specific gravity of a liquid?

9. How does the specific gravity of oil compare with that of water?

10. List four ways to fight an oil fire.

11. Which is lighter, alcohol or water?

12. Why won't alcohol float on water?

ERWIN SCHROEDINGER (1887-1961), Austrian, proposed the modern wave theory of matter, which states that an electron is not really a particle but exists as a wave (similar to light). In 1933, he shared with the English physicist, Paul Adirn Maurice Dirac, the Nobel Prize in physics. Schroedinger wrote about the effect of science upon life. Some of his writings are *Nature and the Greeks, Science and the Human Temperament*, and *What Is Life?*

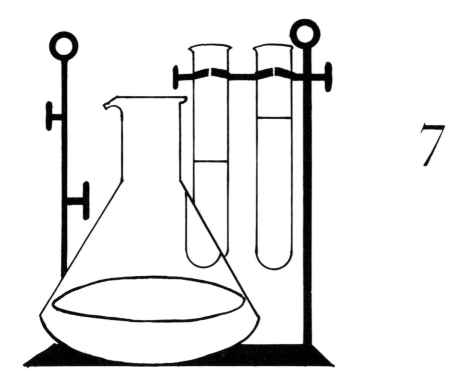

CAN A NEEDLE FLOAT?

Most people believe that if they place a needle into water, it will sink. Usually it will — but it doesn't have to. If you take advantage of a property called *surface tension*, you can make a needle, or even a razor blade, float in water.

MATERIALS: Drinking glass; water; needle or razor blade; small piece of newspaper; two toothpicks; bar of soap.

METHOD: Part I — Place the paper in the water and rest the needle upon it carefully. With the toothpick, try to push the ends of the paper, and then the entire paper, into the water. If done slowly, the paper will sink and the needle will remain floating on what appears to be — but is not — a film (Fig. 7–1). Next, touch the needle with the toothpick — it will sink quickly to the bottom.

Part II — Repeat the experiment. While the needle is floating, let one drop of soapy water fall nearby. What happens?

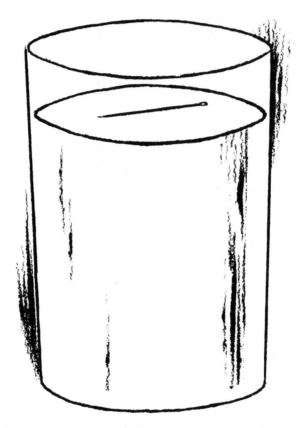

A needle floats in water!
Figure 7–1

DISCUSSION: If a drop of water were to be divided in half and these halves were divided into halves and we continued dividing these drops into smaller and smaller parts, we would eventually reach the smallest particle that existed and could still be called water. This particle is known as a molecule. The story of these molecules and what they are is a wonderful story in itself and part of their history will be discussed later. The reader who is interested in learning more about the behavior of molecules and atoms can find many books on this subject in the library.

It is believed that the molecules of water exist as a liquid because they have a fairly strong attraction for each other. This force of attraction is called *cohesion*. The molecules at the surface of the liquid have nothing attracting them from above; therefore, all of them are pulled toward the molecules below, causing an invisible, tight film which can support the needle. This is called *surface tension*.

It seems incredible that the water molecules can attract each other with sufficient force to hold up a needle. It is the same as if you and some friends of yours were to hold one another's hands. If you hold on tightly enough, you can support a weight.

As the needle floats, observe carefully and you will see that it is floating on *top* of the water. No part of the needle is under water, and the surface is bent under the weight of the needle. This has absolutely nothing to do with buoyancy, which requires that a floating body must sink part of the way into the water to displace an equal weight. The force holding up the needle is due only to the attraction between water molecules.

When the toothpick touches the water, the extra push is enough to force the water molecules apart, causing the needle to sink.

Soap weakens the attraction that water molecules have for each other; this action of soap enables water to wash away dirt more effectively. For dirt to be washed away, it must be attracted to the water molecules. However, the water molecules are attracted to each other more strongly than they are to the dirt. Soap weakens this attraction; water and soap molecules carry the dirt away.

It is always a wonder of science that the explanation of why a needle floats can also help explain something so completely different as why soap helps water clean away dirt.

SELF-TEST
ANSWERS ON PAGE 173

1. What are the smallest particles of water that can exist and still have the properties of water?

2. What is the name of the attractive force that causes molecules of water to remain together as a liquid?

3. The attraction of molecules for each other at the surface of the water forms a tight, invisible film. What is the name given to this effect?

4. When a needle floats in water, is any part of it under water?

5. Is floating a needle on water an example of buoyancy?

6. What enables a needle to float on water?

7. How can the needle be made to sink?

8. Why did the addition of soap cause the needle to sink?

9. What must occur for dirt to be removed effectively?

10. Are water molecules attracted more strongly to themselves than to dirt?

11. Soap lowers the attraction of water molecules for each other. How does this enable dirt to be washed away more easily?

Alchemist In His Laboratory

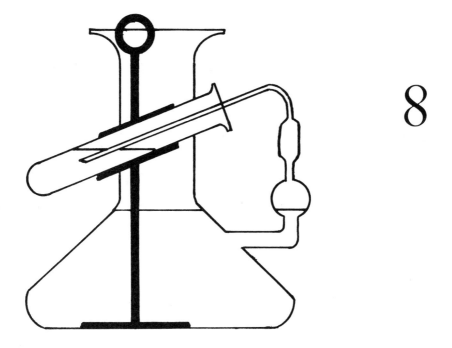

WATER AND SURFACE TENSION

One of the most useful functions of water is that it helps us keep things clean. It can easily dissolve the salt given off by the glands of our skin during perspiration, but it cannot readily wash away the oil that accompanies the salt. In our previous experiment we found that soap lowers the surface tension of water and thus helps it become an excellent cleansing agent. In this experiment we will investigate how various substances lower the surface tension of water, and some of the surprising effects achieved.

MATERIALS: Olive oil; water; rubbing alcohol; pepper; soap;

test tube; butter knife; cardboard; basin; two matchsticks; two drinking glasses.

METHOD: Part I — Pour several drops of olive oil into a test tube, and half fill the tube with water. Place your thumb over the end of the tube and shake vigorously. As was previously observed, the oil and water will separate and the oil will float on top.

With a butter knife, scrape off some shavings from a cake of soap and add to the test tube. Shake vigorously and observe the results. Are two layers present? What do you think happened?

Part II — Rub several drops of oil into the palm of your hand, then wet it with water. Extend your palm and examine the droplets of water. Wash your palm with soap. Did the re-

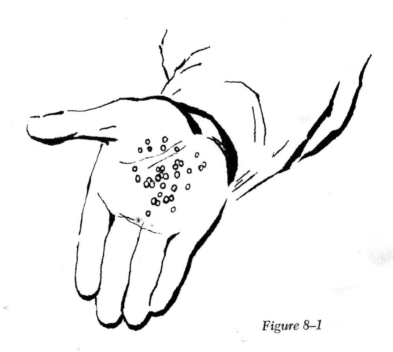

Figure 8–1

sults in Part I help explain the effects of soap when mixed with water? (Fig. 8–1)

Part III — The following experiments seem to have little to do with the role of soap as a cleansing agent. Try them and see if you can explain their effects.

a) Cut a thin piece of wood or a thick piece of cardboard into the shape of a small boat. Cut a notch in the rear and insert a small piece of soap so that it will be halfway in the water (Fig. 8–2). Place the boat in a basin or bathtub of water and it will move mysteriously without outside help.

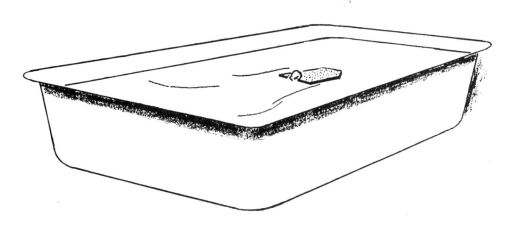

A small boat uses "soap power" to propel itself through the water.

Figure 8–2

b) Place two matchsticks about three-quarters of an inch apart in a pan of water. Allow a drop of rubbing alcohol to fall between them. Which way do they move? Repeat the experiment. This time allow a drop of soap solution to fall between them. Which way do they move? Why? Hint — when water wets a substance, it means that its molecules are attracted to the molecules of that substance. How does this plus the effects of soap on surface tension explain the results? (Fig. 8–3)

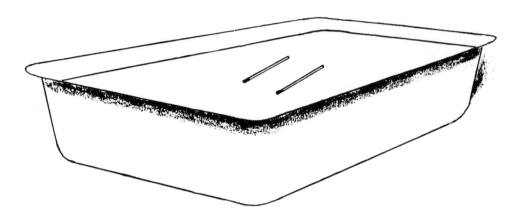

Matchsticks floating in water.

Figure 8–3

c) Pour some pepper into two separate glasses of water. Place your finger into the water in one of the glasses. What happens to the pepper when you take your finger from the glass? Next, rub another finger through your hair several times, and place it into the other glass. What happens to the pepper? (Fig. 8–4)

DISCUSSION: In Part I, we demonstrated that oil and water do not dissolve in each other. The addition of soap caused the two separate layers to disappear and form a cloudy mixture which resembled neither oil nor water. Oil is not soluble in water because the attraction of water molecules for each other is greater than their attraction for oil. This was demonstrated with the oil on your palm and the droplets of water. Since water molecules attracted each other so strongly, they formed small spheres or drops which rolled over the oily surface.

Another way to state that water does not attract oil is to say that water does not *wet* oil. When water is attracted and clings to a surface, it is said to wet it.

Figure 8–4

Soap is attracted to both water and oil. Part of the soap molecule breaks the oil into tiny drops and several molecules surround each drop. Another part of the soap molecule is attracted to the water. As a result, the tiny drops of oil are scattered throughout the water. This mixture is called an *emulsion*. The oil is not dissolved in the water as sugar or table salt would be. However, since the soap keeps the oil drops floating in the water, they can be washed away.

Other examples of emulsions are homogenized milk, which contains droplets of butterfat, and mayonnaise, which contains droplets of vegetable oil. Milk is forced through very tiny holes in order to break the butterfat into droplets so tiny that they have less tendency to come together and become large. To make mayonnaise, vegetable oil is mixed with vinegar and spices and shaken up with egg yolk to prevent the droplets from forming larger drops which would rise.

In Part III a, we saw that soap lowers the surface tension of water. The toy boat in the basin is wet by the water on all sides. Remember that, at the surface, water molecules that are attracted to the boat also attract the water molecules nearest themselves so that there is a continuous chain from one end of the basin to the other. Since the boat is being pulled equally on all sides, it does not move. The addition of soap at the rear of the boat lowers the attraction of the water molecules there for each other. When there is no longer a continuous chain of molecules pulling the boat equally on all sides, the boat moves forward because the water molecules in front are working harder than those in the rear. The boat will move until soap has weakened the surface tension of the entire water surface.

In Part III b, at first the matchsticks do not move because the surface tension of water between them pulls them together with the same force that the water outside pulls them apart. When rubbing alcohol or soap is placed between them, the surface tension between the sticks is lowered and can no longer pull them together. Since the surface tension outside the sticks is undiminished, it pulls them apart.

In Part III c, water wets the pepper and your finger. When

JOHN DALTON (1766-1844), English, is famous for his atomic theories and discoveries of laws which helped explain how substances react with each other. His study of the atmosphere and other gases led him to the discovery of laws concerning gas pressures. In 1794, he wrote about color blindness, from which he suffered. This condition is often called Daltonism. In 1822, he was elected to the Royal Society.

you remove your finger from the water, the water clings to it and the pepper clings to the water on your finger. When you rub your finger through your hair, your finger becomes oily. Water is not attracted to oil. Then, when you place your oily finger in the second glass of water, the water molecules move away, carrying the pepper with them.

SELF-TEST
ANSWERS ON PAGE 173

1. How many layers were formed when oil and water were mixed together?

2. What was the effect of adding soap to the oil and water mixture?

3. What is the effect of adding water to an oily surface?

4. Why doesn't oil dissolve in water?

5. Why doesn't water wet oil?

6. Is soap attracted to both oil and water?

7. What effect does the soap molecule have upon oil?

8. What effect does the soap molecule have upon water?

9. What is the name of the mixture that is formed when soap scatters the tiny drops of oil throughout the water?

10. Is oil actually dissolved in water in an emulsion?

11. Give two examples of emulsions.

12. What is used in mayonnaise to prevent the small drops of oil from coming together and rising?

13. How is homogenized milk made?

14. Why did the toy boat in this experiment move through the water?

15. What happened when soap—or alcohol—was placed between two matchsticks?

16. Why did the matchsticks behave in this manner?

17. Why were grains of pepper attracted to your finger?

18. Why did the pepper move away from your finger after oil had been placed on it?

Alchemist's Laboratory

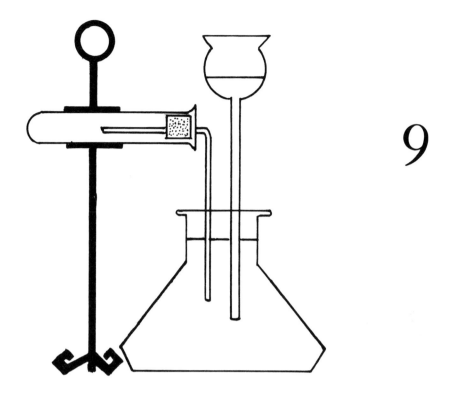

SOAP BUBBLES

Who has not experienced the thrill of producing soap bubbles? These shimmering, colorful spheres are a source of delight to youngsters, but they are also a valuable source of information about molecular attraction. The effects of surface tension can be effectively studied with soap bubbles, for the weight of liquid is small as compared to the strength of the film.

MATERIALS: Soap; water; glycerin; copper wire; thread; glass; needle; clay pipe or straw; candle; glass funnel; balance.

METHOD: Dissolve some soap flakes in hot water. This is adequate for demonstrations, but a stronger and longer lasting film may be produced by adding glycerin which may be obtained in a drugstore. Glycerin is a colorless, odorless, and sticky liquid that resembles water in appearance. It is produced as a by-product during the manufacture of soap, and is used in the manufacture of cosmetics and medicines.

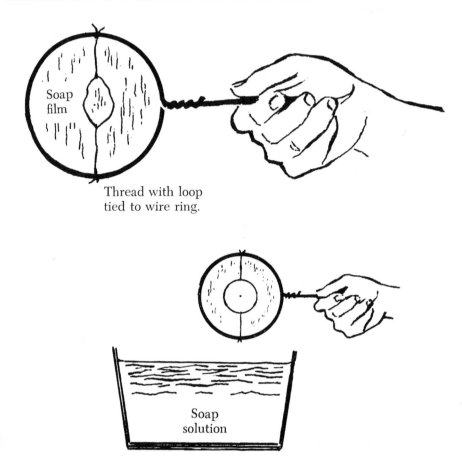

When the film inside the loop of thread is broken, the outer film pulls the loop into the shape of a circle.

Figure 9–1

Part I — Bend the wire into a handle and ring about 3 inches in diameter. Make a small circle or loop of thread about ½ inch wide and tie it across the ring as in Figure 9–1. Produce a film by dipping the ring into the soap solution. What is the shape of the thread loop? Puncture the film inside the thread circle with a needle. It may be necessary to heat the point of the needle. What change occurs in the shape of the loop? Can it be explained by surface tension?

Part II — Blow a bubble with a clay pipe or a drinking straw and close the mouthpiece with your thumb. Direct that end toward the flame of a candle and remove the thumb. What happens to the flame as the bubble changes? What does this prove about liquid surfaces? (Fig. 9–2)

Part III — Cover the tip of a glass funnel with your thumb. Dip the opposite end into the soap solution so that a film forms

Figure 9–2

across the mouth of the funnel. Remove the thumb and observe the action of the film (Fig. 9—3).

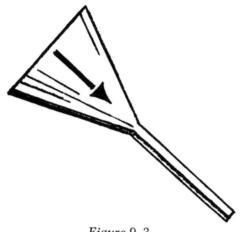

Figure 9–3

Part IV — Make a wire form with a movable wire that has a hook in the center (Fig. 9—4a). Make several U-shaped weights of different sizes from bits of wire. Immerse the frame in the soap solution. Produce a film by pulling on the movable wire (Fig. 9—4c) and observe what happens to the wire as you release it.

Stretch the film by adding the U-shaped weights to the hook (Fig. 9—4d). When a sufficient number of weights has been added, the film will break. Weigh the copper U's and compare the weight to the area of the film. Clean the wire thoroughly and measure the surface tension of tap water. Compare both values.

DISCUSSION: All of the experiments demonstrate the force

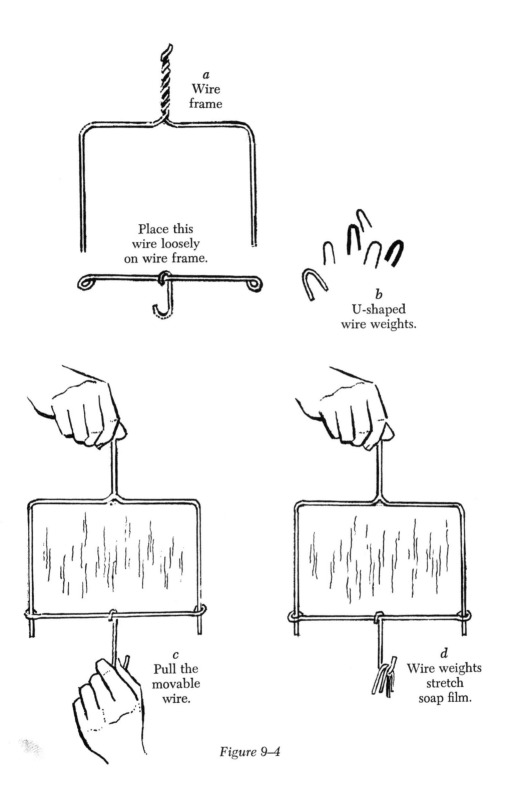

a
Wire frame

Place this wire loosely on wire frame.

b
U-shaped wire weights.

c
Pull the movable wire.

d
Wire weights stretch soap film.

Figure 9–4

(Courtesy Fisher Scientific, Inc.)

GALILEO GALILEI (1564-1642), Italian, discovered the laws of a swinging pendulum. He dropped two heavy objects of different weights from the top of the leaning Tower of Pisa and proved that, except for the resistance of air, all objects fall at the same speed. Galileo studied the heavens with a telescope and stated that the earth travels about the sun. He is recognized as one of the world's greatest scientists and teachers.

of surface tension. In Part I, when the film inside the thread loop is punctured, the loop is drawn out to a circle. The soap film outside the thread tends to become as small as possible and pulls on every part of the loop. Since there is no film pulling back within the loop, it spreads out to form a circle.

In Part II, surface tension makes the bubble as small as possible. As a result, the air is forced out and blows the candle flame away. In Part III, surface tension causes the film to be drawn from the mouth of the funnel to the narrow stem. When the movable wire is released, in Part IV, there is a similar action. Your measurements will show that the surface tension of soap solution is greater than that of tap water. This is the reason that bubbles can be made so easily with soap solution.

1. Why can soap bubbles be effectively used in the study of surface tension?

2. What can be added to a soap solution to produce a stronger film?

3. Does a film try to become larger or smaller because of surface tension?

4. Is it possible to measure the amount of surface tension present in a liquid?

5. How does the surface tension of a soap solution compare with that of water?

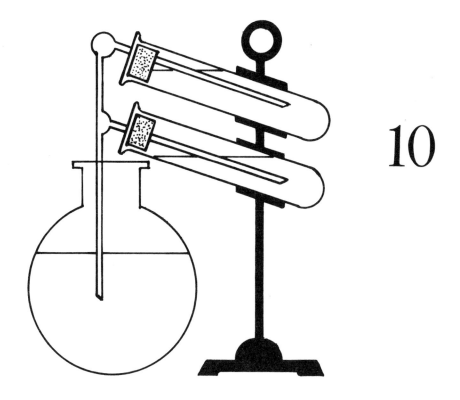

10

ADHESION AND CAPILLARY ACTION

Water molecules are strongly attracted to each other. The force of attraction among molecules of a single substance is called *cohesion*. Water wets another substance because the water molecules are attracted to that substance. The force of attraction among molecules of different substances is called *adhesion*. It should be noted, however, that the force which causes adhesion is the same as the force that causes cohesion. Sometimes adhesive forces are stronger than cohesive forces. When a broken piece of wood is mended with glue, the forces of adhesion between the wood and the glue are so strong that the wood will often break more easily than the joint that was repaired.

Adhesive forces are present everywhere. They enable a pencil mark to stick to paper or paint to adhere to a wall, and they allow cloth to absorb dye through a process called capillary action. This action will be discussed after observing its behavior in the next experiments. We will discover how adhesive forces operate and how useful they can be.

MATERIALS: Two flat glass plates; water; mercury; oil; rubber band; toothpick; glass tube (¼ inch opening); capillary tube (a glass tube with a very small opening — Fig. 10–5a).

METHOD: Part I — Immerse a clean piece of glass in water. Why does the water cling to the glass upon removal, instead of remaining with the other water molecules? Dip the glass in mercury, which is a heavy, silvery liquid metal used to make thermometers. Does the mercury cling to the glass?

Part II — Rub some oil on a piece of glass and dip it into the water. Does the water wet the glass? Why? Refer to the discussion on page **66**.

Part III — Wet two glass plates; then place them together. Try to separate them by holding one down and attempting to lift the other straight up. What type of force holds the glasses together?

Part IV — Attach a rubber band to the center of a glass plate with adhesive tape. Lower the glass to the surface of the water, then lift gently (Fig. 10–1). How would you measure the attraction between the glass and the water?

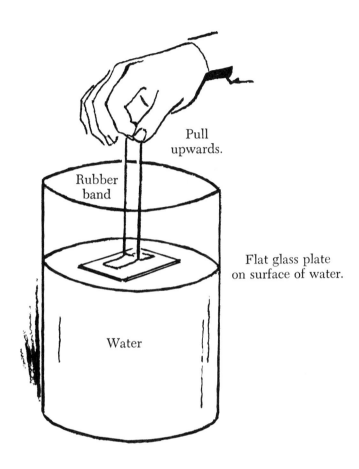

What happens as you attempt to lift the glass plate?

Figure 10–1

Part V — Place both glass plates into the water and hold them together at one end. Separate the opposite ends with a toothpick. What happens to the water between the glass plates?

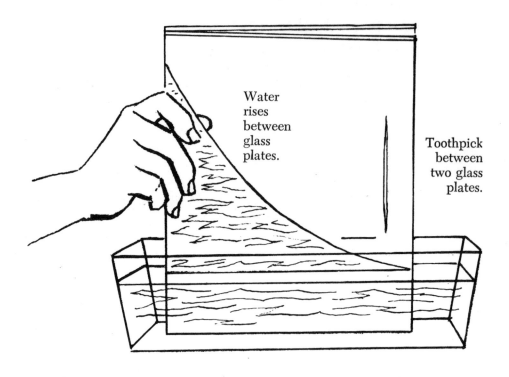

Water
rises
between
glass
plates.

Toothpick
between
two glass
plates.

Figure 10–2

Squeeze the ends separated by the toothpick (Fig. 10–2). What are your conclusions?

Part VI — a) Place a glass tube that has a ¼ inch opening into the water in a vertical position (Fig. 10–3). Compare the height of the water in the tube to the height outside. Observe the top of the water inside the tube. Is it flat? Look closely at the level of the water where it touches the outside of the tube. What forces are involved?

b) Perform the experiment with mercury instead of water (Fig. 10–4). Why is their behavior so different?

c) Capillary tubes are used to make thermometers and

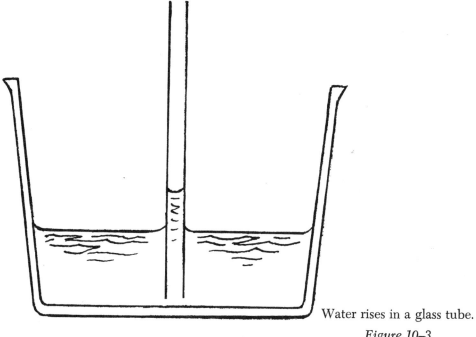

Water rises in a glass tube.

Figure 10–3

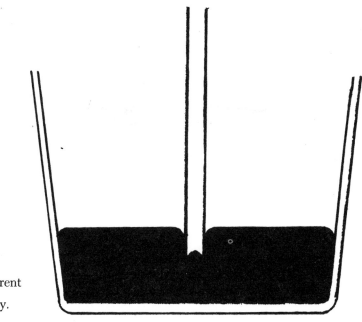

Observe the different
levels of mercury.

Figure 10–4

have very narrow openings (Fig. 10–5a). They are available at science supply houses, or perhaps your pharmacist has the remains of a broken thermometer you may use. Place the tube upright in the water. From the results obtained in Part IV, what do you suppose will happen? (Fig. 10–5b)

d) Perform the experiment with mercury and compare its action to that of water (Fig. 10–5c).

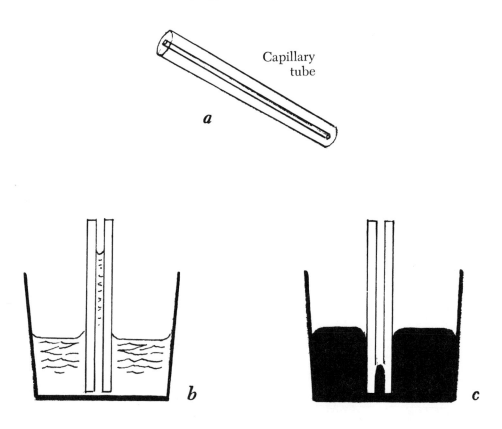

Observe the height of the liquid in each tube.

Figure 10–5

DISCUSSION: In Part I, the glass was wet because, as was previously discussed, the water molecules were attracted to the glass. If their self-attraction, also called cohesive force, had been greater than their attraction to the glass — or adhesive force — they would not have wet the glass. This is clearly demonstrated when glass is placed in mercury. Upon removal, the mercury remains with the main body of liquid and the glass emerges dry.

A similar situation occurred in Part II, when oiled glass was not wet by water. A candle, when placed in water, will act the same way, for the molecules of the candle are very similar to the molecules of oil.

It was surprisingly difficult to separate the glass plates in Part III, indicating that the forces holding them together were quite powerful. Are we demonstrating adhesion or cohesion? Does only the water hold the glass plates together? We had defined adhesion as attraction between different substances. Upon examining the glass plates, we note that the water molecules still cling to each plate. It is clear, therefore, that the water molecules clinging to one plate (adhesion) were merely separated from the water molecules clinging to the other plate. Thus, we demonstrated that the force of cohesion between water molecules was more easily overcome than the force of adhesion between water and glass.

In Part IV, we demonstrated the force necessary to pull the glass from the water. You will agree, no doubt, that we are measuring, once more, the forces of cohesion. As before, the water that remains with the glass had to break away from the main body of water. These experiments all indicate that the adhesive forces between water and glass are greater than the cohesive forces.

How can we, then, measure adhesion? In Part V we observed that the water rose between the glass plates — against

BENJAMIN THOMPSON (COUNT RUMFORD) (1753-1814), experimented with gunpowder, improved firearms, and studied the absorption of moisture by certain substances. His most important work was in determining the nature of heat, which at that time was thought to be an indestructible fluid. However, his experiments convinced him that heat was not a separate substance but was a form of motion of the tiny particles that make up a substance.

the force of gravity! The narrower the space between the glass plates, the higher the water rose. This is known as *capillarity* or *capillary action*. We can assume that the water rose because it was attracted to the glass, demonstrating adhesion. But why doesn't the water continue to rise and go over the top? For the answer, observe the narrow capillary tube in Part VI.

The surface of the water in the tube is curved because the water molecules next to the glass are being attracted away from the main body of water, and rise. They, in turn, attract the water molecules next to them — through cohesion — and pull them along. These molecules are actually getting a free ride upward for they are too far from the glass to be attracted to it with enough force to overcome gravity. As the water next to the glass moves higher and higher, it drags along more and more water through cohesion. Two opposing forces are working. Adhesion is pulling upward and gravity is pulling downward. The water column is not pulled apart because of cohesion. When the forces pulling up are equal to the weight of the column of water pulling down, the water stops rising. The narrower the tube, the higher the water will rise because it weighs less and is easier to lift than a wide column. Blotting paper, towels, cotton, and other absorbent materials make use of capillary action to soak up liquids.

Exactly the opposite occurs with mercury. When a capillary tube is placed in mercury, the level in the tube is lower and the surface of the mercury curves away from the glass. This indicates that the cohesive forces among mercury molecules are much greater than the very weak adhesive forces between mercury and glass.

SELF-TEST
ANSWERS ON PAGE **174**

1. What is adhesion?

2. Can forces of adhesion sometimes be stronger than forces of cohesion?

3. Water wets glass. Is this considered adhesion or cohesion?

4. Does liquid mercury wet glass?

5. It is difficult to separate two flat glass plates that are wet. What type of force does this illustrate?

6. Give an example of capillary action.

7. Why can't water in a capillary tube rise indefinitely?

8. Which will rise higher due to capillary action, a narrow column of water or a wide column?

9. Does mercury rise in a capillary tube?

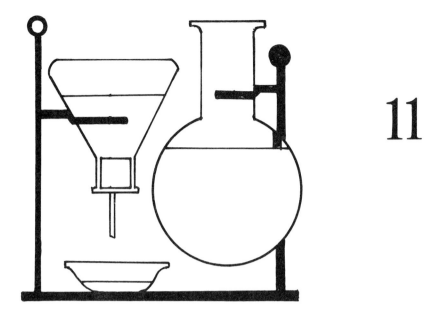

PERPETUAL MOTION—AT LAST?

The patent office no longer accepts applications from inventors of perpetual motion machines. It has been proven again and again experimentally, theoretically, mathematically, and dogmatically, that perpetual motion is impossible. The perpetual motion machines included in this section are based on capillary action. Will they work forever? The young — and old — scientist is challenged to find the answer.

MATERIALS: Two water glasses; battery jar (or large jar in the form of a cylinder), fish tank, or bell jar; tape; capillary tubes; water.

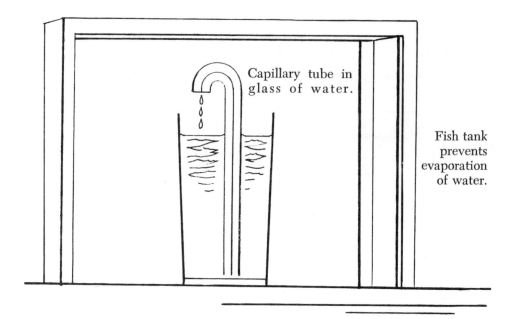

Capillary tube in glass of water.

Fish tank prevents evaporation of water.

Will this ever stop?
Figure 11–1

METHOD: Part I — Construct the apparatus as illustrated in Figure 11–1. A capillary tube can be bent in the heat of a bunsen burner; your teacher or pharmacist can do it in a few minutes. If you prefer you may leave it straight. The glass jar surrounding the glass of water is sealed with wax, glue, or tape to prevent evaporation of water. It also prevents heat from entering the system so that no "outside" help is available. Though not the best insulator, it is used in this experiment for easy visibility. Water will rise in the capillary tube until it reaches the end of the curved portion, where it will fall, to be used again and again and . . . ?

Part II — Arrange two capillary tubes as illustrated in Figure 11–2. The water in glass No. 1 will rise in the capillary tube and fall into glass No. 2. At the same time, the water will rise in glass No. 2 and fall into glass No. 1. It may seem that, since the tubes cannot be exactly alike in length and width, the motion will stop when one glass is emptied. However, when this occurs, the water in the other glass will begin to fill it again and capillary action will resume by itself.

Will either of these actions ever stop? The answer, of course, is *yes*, but only under very special conditions. In fact, by using a glass cover to prevent evaporation, as we have done in this experiment, it may never stop.

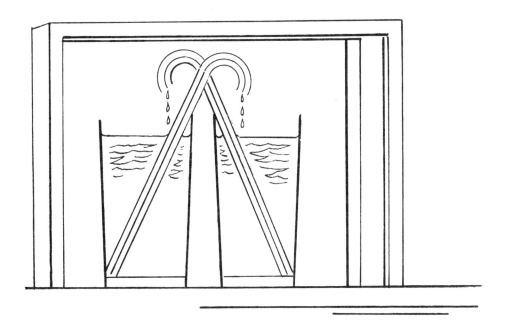

Perhaps you prefer this version.

Figure 11–2

DISCUSSION: The conditions of perpetual motion require that a system will remain in motion forever without outside help. Friction prevents perpetual motion since friction causes energy

(Wide World Photos Inc.)

NIELS BOHR (1885-1962), Danish, escaped from German-occupied Denmark in 1943. He reached the United States where he took part in the atomic bomb project at Los Alamos, New Mexico. He made important advances in our knowledge of atomic structure. In 1922, he was awarded the Nobel Prize in physics. Bohr also received the first Atoms for Peace Award in 1957. In 1920, Bohr founded the Copenhagen Institute for Theoretical Physics and was its head until 1962.

to be lost in the form of heat. You can demonstrate this by rubbing your hands together rapidly. A wheel would turn forever if it did not lose its energy (in the form of heat) due to friction. The earth moves forever around the sun because it travels through space without rubbing against anything.*

When the water rises in the capillary tube a small amount of friction occurs between the water and the glass and between the water molecules themselves. The heat that is produced is slowly lost to the surrounding atmosphere. This causes the water and the tube to become colder. The process continues until the water freezes — and "perpetual" motion ends. However, in this experiment the water will not freeze because as soon as it becomes slightly colder than its surroundings, the warmer air and sunlight supply it with additional heat. Unless this is prevented (it requires lots of effort) water will continue to rise in the capillary tube. Nevertheless, this is not considered true perpetual motion because of the "outside" help.

*There is actually a minute amount of friction produced due to the dust particles in space.

SELF-TEST

ANSWERS ON PAGE **174**

1. What is perpetual motion?

2. What prevents perpetual motion?

3. If there were no friction, could a wheel turn forever?

4. Why should the water in the capillary tube eventually stop rising?

5. Why will the water in this experiment continue to rise as if it were perpetual motion?

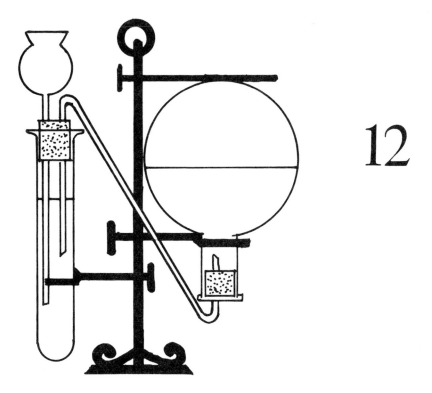

12

WATER AND LIGHT

What is light and how is it related to our study of water? Light comes to us from various sources — a light bulb, a burning match, or from the sun. It is essential to plants so that they can carry on life and make food which we use so that we can carry on life. It travels through gases and liquids and through solids such as glass and certain plastics. When it cannot pass through a solid, it bounces away, or is captured and changed to heat, or causes a chemical reaction.

These are some of the things that light *does,* but what *is* it? Scientists have pondered the question for many years and have come up with complicated answers. They say it is a form of energy which enables us to see, or do work. Experiments suggest that it consists of particles traveling through space at approximately 186,000 miles per second. On the other hand, many experiments indicate that it consists of waves traveling through space, like the ripple or wave that travels across a stream when you throw a rock into the water. But a ripple is carried by water. What carries a light wave? We know it is not air, for light can travel through a vacuum; in fact it moves faster. Its mode of travel is a deep mystery, for a vacuum seems to contain nothing that can carry a light wave. Scientists believe that light consists of separate "bundles" of waves; it acts as if it consists of separate particles — and each particle acts like a wave.

When light travels through glass or water it slows down, resulting in interesting effects which we will study. In this series of experiments, we will examine what happens when light waves and water act upon each other.

MATERIALS: Cardboard; flashlight; cellophane tape; aluminum foil; fish tank; water; milk; pencil; drinking glass; nail; a tin can, as directed in experiment 1, page 14.

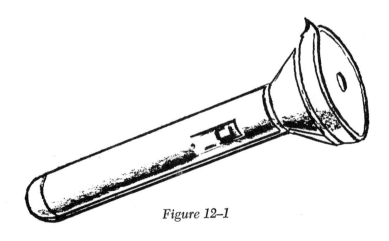

Figure 12–1

ANTON VAN LEEUWENHOEK (1632-1723), Dutch, learned to build a microscope that enabled him to see tiny organisms never before visible to man. He ground and mounted his own lenses, and was the first to see red blood cells. He made hundreds of accurate drawings of the minute cells that make up plants, heart muscles, and many types of bacteria.

METHOD: Part I — Cut a circle of cardboard large enough to fit over a flashlight and punch a hole about one half inch wide in the center. Fasten the cardboard circle to the face of the flashlight with cellophane tape (Fig. 12–1). This will enable you to produce a narrow beam of light. Place a mirror or a smooth sheet of aluminum foil at the bottom of the fish tank to act as a mirror. Fill the tank halfway with water and add several drops of milk. Ignite a small piece of newspaper and move it across the liquid, then drop it into a sink. Cover the tank with a glass top. The smoke above the water will help you to follow the beam of light as it passes through air, and the milk will enable you to see the path of the beam as it passes through the water.

a) Direct the beam of light straight down through the water as at A, Figure 12–2. What is the direction of the beam as it goes through the water? Stir the water and observe the beam.

b) Direct the light beam at an angle as at B and observe the beam of light. Change the direction of the light beam toward C (Fig. 12–2). Stir the water and observe the beam of light.

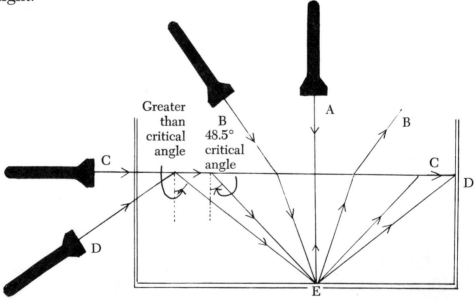

A drop or two of milk in the water will enable you to follow the path of the light.

Figure 12–2

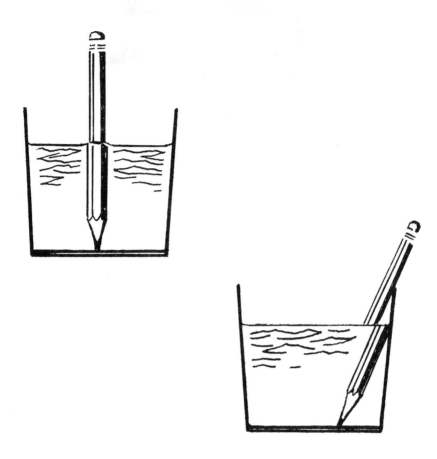

Figure 12–3

c) Now hold the flashlight outside the tank and below the level of the liquid, changing the angle of the flashlight from almost horizontal at C, toward D and E. At what angle is there a sudden change?

Part II — The following effects are based on the effects observed in **Part I** a, b, c.

a) Place a pencil straight down into a glass of water (Fig. 12–3). Allow another pencil to lean against the side. Can you explain what happens?

b) Make a magnifying lens with thick alumium foil or a piece of metal from a discarded can. Place the aluminum on a block of wood and punch a sharp round hole through it with a moderately large nail. Place a drop of water in the hole and you will have an excellent magnifying lens (Fig. 12–4). A small amount of vaseline or oil around the edges of the hole will help form a spherical drop of water.

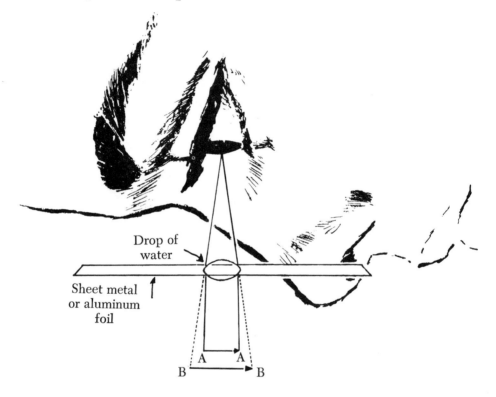

Figure 12–4

c) Hold a glass of water above your head and dip the head of a nail into the water as you look at the nail from below (Fig. 12–5). You will be able to see the reflection of the nail from the mirror-like undersurface of the water. Move the nail up and down slowly. As you lower the nail, the image moves upward. And, as expected, the reverse occurs when the nail is raised. How does this relate to the results obtained in Part I c? Shake the glass. What happens to the image?

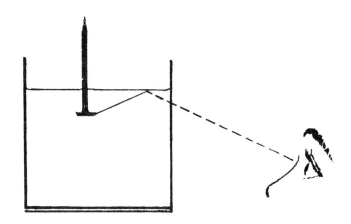

Observe the reflection of the nail as you move it up and down.

Figure 12–5

d) Use the can in experiment 1, page 14. Darken the room and direct the full flashlight beam into the water. What is the appearance of the streams of water as they leave the can? Can any of the experiments in Part I be used to explain this effect?

e) Place a penny in a soup bowl and place the bowl in front of you so that the sides barely hide the coin from view. Add water slowly. Why does the coin suddenly appear? (Fig. 12–6).

DISCUSSION: A beam of light traveling through air moves in a straight line. This is illustrated in Figure 12–2. Follow rays

A, B, C, and D as they enter the water and as they leave. At the surface, where air and water meet, there is a bending or change in direction of the light beam. As the flashlight is brought closer to the horizontal, the amount of bending that takes place increases. The bending of light when it passes from one medium, such as water, to another medium, such as air, is called *refraction*.

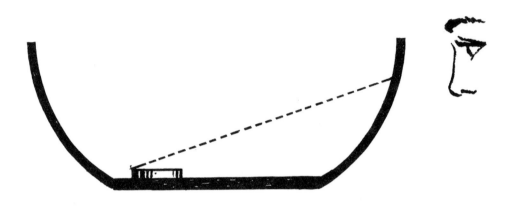

Side of cup prevents image of coin from reaching eye.
Figure 12-6a

The rays are observed to travel to the mirror at the bottom of the tank and bounce upward the way a ball would bounce if it were thrown at an angle. This is called *reflection*. As the beam of light passes from the water to the air, it is bent once more. A surprising thing happens to ray D. Instead of passing upward through the surface of the water, it is almost totally reflected. The undersurface of the water acts like a mirror. The angle at which this begins to occur — 48.5° — is called the critical angle.

How is a fish's viewpoint affected by all of this? Imagine a fish at E at the bottom of the tank. He can see through the water up to ray C. Beyond that, all he can see is the reflection of the bottom of the tank. A fish's-eye view is a circular window above him. Beyond the "edges" of his window he can only see reflections of the bottom. On a day when the water is rough, a fish sees a broken image. This was illustrated in Part I, a and b, when the water was stirred. A fisherman is, therefore, usually more successful on a windy day when the water is disturbed and he cannot be seen.

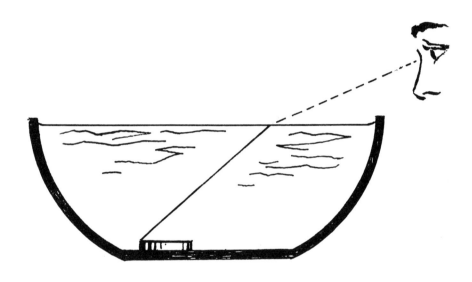

Water in cup bends light ray so that image reaches eye.
Figure 12-6b

What is the cause of refraction? Measurements have shown that light travels through water at a speed of 140,000 miles per second as compared with 186,000 miles per second in air. This difference in speed causes the bending of light. This can be explained by assuming that light travels as a wave (Fig.

12–7a). As it passes from air to water, the left side of the wave,

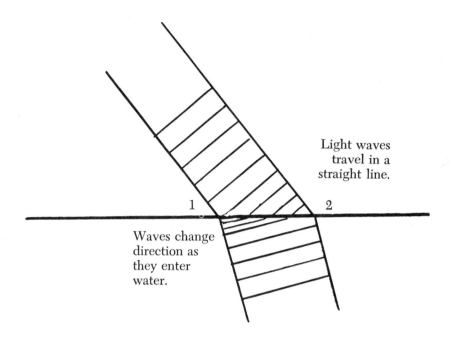

Figure 12–7a

labeled 1, reaches the water first, and that portion of the wave slows down. However, the right side, marked 2, is still going as fast as before. As a result, there is a change in direction until the entire wave is in the water. This can be compared to a toy automobile which is rolled along a wooden floor at an angle to a rug (Fig. 12–7b). The left wheel slows down as it reaches the rug, while the right wheel keeps moving quickly. As a result, the direction changes.

In Part II a, the pencils appear as they do because the light from the pencils in the water bends as it passes to the air. The pencil leaning against the side seems broken. The upright pencil appears magnified under water because its light is bent as it passes through the curved glass which acts like a spherical drop of water. In Part II b, the drop of water acts as a magnifying glass because it is curved. Follow the rays in Figure 12–4. The light from image AA is bent as it passes from air to water and from water back to air. As a result, the light reaches the eye at an angle instead of straight from the object. Because of this, the brain "sees" it as having started at BB. Therefore, the image appears larger.

In Part II d, a number of light waves leave through the opening in the can. Many of these rays reach the boundaries

This side of automobile continues to move quickly as rug slows down other side.

Figure 12–7b

of the streams of water at angles greater than the critical angle and cannot escape. Instead, they bounce along the stream until they reach an angle that permits them to leave. Those that do not find a way out keep bouncing back and forth until they reach the end of the stream.

In Part II e, the coin will suddenly appear when sufficient water is added. The light from the coin goes up through the water and is bent upon reaching the air. When the water level is low, the light is stopped by the sides of the bowl. When the level is high enough, the beam is bent nearer the top of the bowl, so that it will escape its sides and reach the eye.

SELF-TEST
ANSWERS ON PAGE **174**

1. Why is light considered to be a form of energy?

2. What two things may light consist of?

3. How fast does light travel through air?

4. Compare the speed of light in water and in air.

5. Can a light wave travel through a vacuum?

6. In what direction does a beam of light travel from its source?

7. What happens when light travels from air to water?

8. In this experiment, as the beam of light is brought to an angle closer to the surface of the water, what effect is there on the amount of bending that occurs?

9. What is refraction?

10. Light bounces like a rubber ball when it hits a smooth surface. What is this effect called?

11. Above a certain angle, light is reflected downward from the undersurface of water. What name is given to this angle?

12. Does a fish see a good image when the water is rough?

13. What is the cause of refraction when light passes from air to water?

14. Why does a pencil appear to be broken when part of it is in water?

15. In Figure 12–5, why is the image of the nail reflected downward?

16. What enables a drop of water to act as a magnifier?

17. In Part II d, why are the streams of water lit up as they leave the can?

18. In Figure 12–6, what causes the coin to appear suddenly as water is added?

THOMAS ALVA EDISON (1847-1931), American, was the greatest inventor the world has ever known. As a boy, he spent his spare time experimenting with electricity and all sorts of mechanical apparatus in a laboratory that he had set up in a baggage car. His inventions include the phonograph, talking pictures, the Edison storage battery, and the mimeograph. His most important invention was the electric light bulb which changed our way of life.

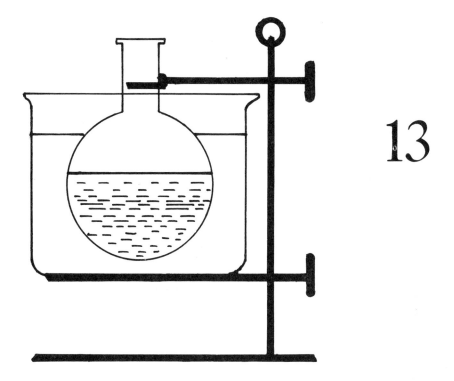

WATER, LIGHT, AND COLOR

We have observed the bending and reflection of light under a variety of conditions. There is another property of light which is perhaps even more striking and exciting. It is the scattering of light into separate colors. The rainbow that we sometimes see is so beautiful that men have made up many stories about this mystery of nature. As scientists, we are going to explore the reasons behind the formation of rainbows.

MATERIALS: Fish tank or basin; mirror; water; flashlight; pane of glass, one foot square; cardboard screen, one foot square.

METHOD: Part I — a) Half fill the basin with water and rest a mirror against the side as shown (Fig. 13–1). Direct the beam of light toward the surface of the mirror. At the proper angle, the light will form a continuous series of rainbow colors on the white cardboard screen. In what order are the colors?

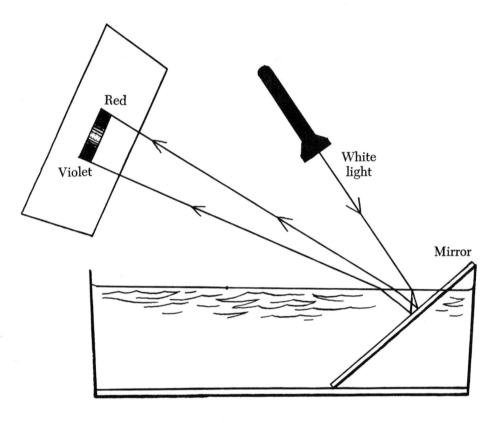

Figure 13–1

b) Instead of a flashlight, you may use the sun as a source of light. Cut a hole about one inch wide in a piece of cardboard and direct the light to the mirror. Change the angle of the mirror until the colors are produced. How do these colors compare to those produced with the flashlight?

Part II — Cool a flat glass pane, one foot square, in a refrigerator. After removing, breathe on the glass so that the water vapor of your breath condenses upon it. Place a flash-

(Courtesy U.S. Weather Bureau.)

How is a rainbow formed?

light on a table, move back several feet, and observe its light through the condensation on the glass.

Part III — Direct a strong beam of light from a bulb or sunlight, through a hole in a piece of cardboard, toward a glass of water (Fig. 13–2). Vary the angle until the light is broken into rainbow colors. In what order are the colors? How does this explain the cause of a rainbow when there are water drops in the air?

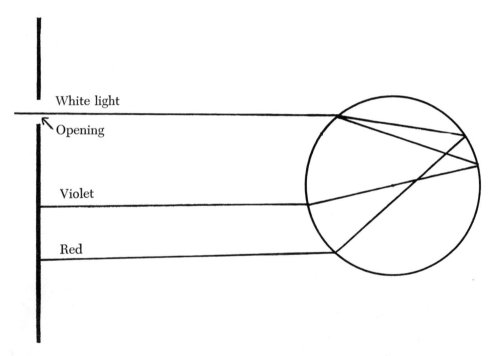

Dispersion of light by a raindrop or by a tumbler of water.

Figure 13–2

DISCUSSION: In 1666, Sir Isaac Newton was experimenting with light. He passed a narrow beam of sunlight through a

MICHAEL FARADAY (1791-1867), English, discovered how electricity could be produced through the use of magnetism. Thus, he introduced the age of electricity. He studied the effects of electric current upon substances in solution. He also worked with light and investigated the properties of gases. He discovered benzene and was the first to change chlorine gas and carbon dioxide gas to liquids.

glass triangle commonly known as a prism. As the beam passed through the prism it was bent twice, but instead of emerging as white light, it spread out to form an array of rainbow colors. These colors are now called the *spectrum,* and the separation

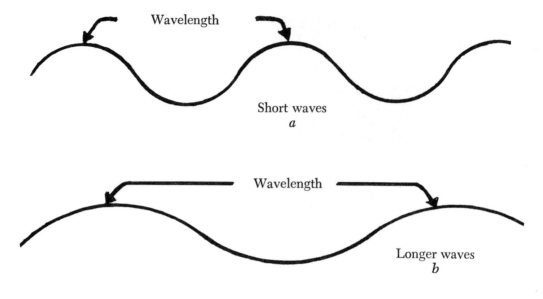

Short waves
a

Longer waves
b

Figure 13–3

of light is called *dispersion.*

The explanation appeared to be that white light was a mixture of colors. However, wasn't it just as reasonable to assume that the glass, in some unknown manner, was able to change white light into different colors? To answer this question, he directed the spectrum through another prism so that the colors would be bent toward each other. The result was white light!

What was the explanation of this remarkable effect? Could it be linked with the natural rainbow? It was soon observed that the order of the colors in the spectrum was identical to that of a rainbow.

In order to understand the explanation we must know what a *wavelength* is. The length of a wave is the distance from one crest to another (Fig. 13–3).

It is believed that light consists of different wavelengths and that each wavelength appears to our eyes as a separate color. The colors of the spectrum are red, orange, yellow, green, blue, indigo, and violet. Red has the longest wavelength and violet has the shortest. When all the colors are mixed in equal amounts they appear as white.

When water bends the same beam of light more than once and at large angles, the colors spread. This is because shorter wavelengths — violet, for example — are bent more than longer wavelengths such as red (Figs. 13–1, 13–2).

Part II demonstrates how white light is dispersed by droplets of water. The glass of water in Part III, though much larger than a single drop, acts the same way and serves to point out how a natural rainbow is formed.

1. What is a prism?

2. As light passes through a prism, it spreads out to form an array of colors. What scientific name is given to these colors?

3. What is dispersion?

4. What does white light consist of?

5. How are the colors of the spectrum related to those of the rainbow?

6. What is meant by wavelength?

7. How do different wavelengths of light appear to our eyes?

8. Are short wavelengths of light bent the same as long wavelengths?

9. What is the shortest wavelength of light?

10. How do raindrops form a rainbow?

DOES HOT WATER WEIGH
THE SAME AS COLD WATER?

Strange though it seems, the fact is that hot water and cold water have different weights, and we can prove it by experiment.

What comparison will we use? Are we going to weigh a cup of hot water and compare it to the weight of a tubful of cold water? In the experiment with oil and water on page 51, we discovered that, to compare the weight of different substances we must compare equal volumes.

Another interesting question that arises is — what happens when hot and cold water meet? Do they simply mix? As you will see, the meeting of hot and cold water produces some very interesting results.

MATERIALS: Small juice glass; hot and cold water; balance; juice can; fish tank; clay; ink; sheet rubber (balloon); rubber bands; candle; beaker; paper; soda bottle; glass tube with one-hole stopper.

METHOD: Part I — To be assured that our volume is the same for both determinations, and because there is no need to use expensive equipment, we can use the same glass for each determination.

a) Paste a label about one quarter of an inch down from the top edge of the glass. Weigh it as accurately as possible and record the weight.

b) Cool some water with ice cubes and pour the water into the glass up to the top of the label. Weigh and record. The weight of the cold water is found by subtracting the weight of the glass from the weight of water plus glass.

c) Fill the glass to the same mark with hot water. Weigh and record. How does the weight of hot water compare with that of cold? Would you expect it to weigh more because of the added heat?

Part II — Punch a hole near the bottom of a small juice can and plug it with a piece of chewing gum or clay. Add a small amount of ink or dye to the can and fill it with hot water. Cover the can with sheet rubber and fasten it to the top of the can with rubber bands. Make a small hole in the center of the rubber sheet, with a nail. Place it in a tank of cold water and remove the plug from the can (Fig. 14–1). Do the results obtained in Part I help explain what happens?

Figure 14–1

Part III — Add some torn bits of paper to a beaker of water. Heat one side of the beaker with a candle as illustrated in Figure 14–2. Observe the circular motion of the paper. Allow the water to cool to room temperature. What happens to the paper?

Part IV — Place the one-hole stopper and glass tube into a small soda bottle full of water. As you press down, some water will enter the glass tube. Mark the height of the water with a rubber band. Heat the bottle with a candle and note what happens to the water in the tube (Fig. 14–3). Place the bottle in ice water. How does this experiment illustrate why cold water weighs more than hot water?

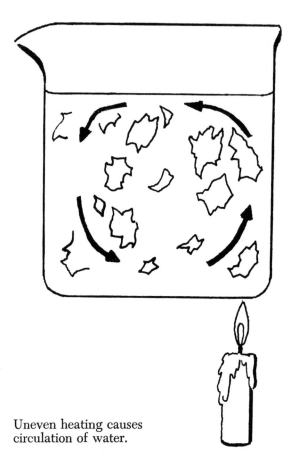

Uneven heating causes circulation of water.

Figure 14–2

DISCUSSION: Measurements in Part I of this experiment demonstrate that cold water weighs more than an equal volume of hot water. Once this has been established, the events in Parts II, III, and IV become clear.

In our buoyancy experiments we saw that objects lighter

than an equal volume of water will float. This applied to liquids and solids (oil or wood in water). If we extend our reasoning, we ought to find that since hot water is lighter than cold water, it, too, will float. That this occurs was demonstrated in Part II. The heavier cold water entered the hole at the bottom of the can and pushed up the lighter hot water. A narrow, colored

Why does the water
rise in the tube?

Figure 14–3

stream was seen to rise from the small hole in the cover of the can. It moved toward the opposite side and sank as it cooled. Thus a current was created in the water. This type of current is called a *convection* current and is one important cause of currents in natural bodies of water. Other causes are winds (which are convection currents of air), earthquakes, the rotation of the earth, and tides caused by the gravitational attraction of the moon (and the sun to a lesser extent).

In Part III, the paper pellets moved in a circle because of convection currents. As the water was heated at one side, it became lighter and was pushed up by the cold water. As the water rose, it carried the paper upward. The cooler water at the other side carried the paper downward as it sank. The water was reheated and rose again. This continuous process resulted in a steady flow of current. When it was allowed to cool, the top and sides cooled unevenly, resulting in a turbulent current flow.

Part IV demonstrated why hot water becomes lighter than cold water. There was, at the beginning of the experiment, a certain weight of water in the bottle. When the water was heated, some of it entered the glass tube indicating that the water had expanded. However, the bottle was still full and since we know it contains less water it must weigh less. Upon cooling, the water contracted and the level in the glass tube dropped as the water entered the bottle.

During the seventeenth century, some clever scientists reasoned that this was a fine way to measure temperature. As the temperature increases, the water expands and rises in a tube. By making the tube very narrow, the water will rise high with even the slight expansion caused by a small increase in temperature; and it will fall with a decrease in temperature.

(Courtesy Fisher Scientific, Inc.)

HENRY CAVENDISH (1731-1810), English. His earliest experiments concerned themselves with the study of the heat produced when a liquid is frozen or when a gas condenses to a liquid. In 1766, he discovered the element, hydrogen, and studied its properties. Later, he was able to determine the composition of the atmosphere. He also discovered that water is composed of hydrogen and oxygen, and proved it by producing it in the laboratory.

Despite this, water was abandoned as a means of measuring temperature. It has a narrow range of usefulness; it cannot be used above its boiling point and it cannot be used at low temperatures for it freezes too soon. It has been replaced by mercury which can be used at fairly high temperatures. Even mercury has its limitations, for at very high temperatures it, too, boils and the mercury thermometer must be replaced by a gas thermometer (which expands upon heating and contracts upon cooling). Also, mercury freezes at approximately 40° below zero Fahrenheit, and must be replaced by alcohol, which is usually dyed red for easy visibility.

Why do liquids — even solids and gases — expand upon heating? As was discussed, water is made up of billions and trillions of tiny molecules. Each of these molecules is in constant motion, vibrating in every direction as they collide with each other billions of times per second.

The movement of the molecules is the energy that we measure with a thermometer. When we heat water, its molecules receive more energy, which means they move faster. These moving molecules bombard the molecules of mercury (or alcohol) in the thermometer, causing them to speed up. As a result, the mercury expands just as water did when it was heated in Part IV, and we note a "rise" in temperature. Accurate measurements require that we take into consideration the slight expansion of the glass.

But why does a substance expand upon being heated? As the speed of the molecules increases, they hit each other harder and harder and bounce further; therefore, there is more space between them and the total volume is greater. As a substance is cooled, the molecules slow down. They no longer bounce as far and are closer together; thus more of them will fit in a container with a resulting increase in weight.

In a lake, for instance, the water is colder at the bottom (unless, of course, it is being fed by a warmer underground stream). In the winter, as the top of the water gets colder, it sinks and the warmer water under it floats to the top. *But* — think of a lake in the wintertime! The ice is on *top* of the warmer water. What happened to our very logical explanation? And what about our experiments? Didn't we find that cold water sinks and hot water rises? Nevertheless, ice floats and there must be a sensible reason. First, we must assume that ice is lighter than an equal volume of water or it would sink. It follows that when water freezes — it expands! It is one of the few substances in nature that acts this way.

Through accurate experiments, scientists have found that water contracts as it cools until it reaches 4° Centigrade (39.2° Fahrenheit). Then it begins to expand until it freezes at 0° C. (32° F.). This occurs because as the water becomes ice, the molecules join in such a way that there is lots of empty space in their crystals. It is as if a crowd of people close together and moving freely — as in a liquid — were to slow down, spread out, and join hands — as in the formation of ice. They would take up more room and weigh less than an equal volume of freely moving "crowd."

This seemingly insignificant fact is fortunate for us, for otherwise we wouldn't be here. In the wintertime, the water is cooled and becomes ice. If ice were heavier than water, it would sink to the bottom and remain there. Very little heat of the sun can penetrate to the depths of a lake or an ocean. The following winter, more ice would form and sink. This would continue until all the waters of the earth became solid ice — and there would be no life as we know it.

1. How can we compare the weights of different substances?
2. Compare the weights of hot water and cold water.
3. Can hot water float on cold water?
4. What is a convection current?
5. What are some causes of currents in water?
6. Why does a quart of hot water weigh less than a quart of cold water?
7. Why is water a poor substance to use in a thermometer?
8. What is actually measured by a thermometer?
9. Why does ice float?
10. At what temperature does water freeze?
11. Why is ice lighter than water?

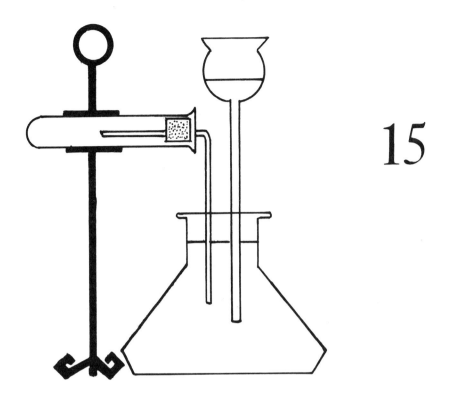

15

IS THERE A DIFFERENCE BETWEEN TEMPERATURE AND HEAT?

In the previous section we saw that the thermometer, in measuring temperature, actually measures the energy of the molecules as they vibrate in all directions. If true, should not a thimbleful of hot water and a basin of hot water be equally effective in heating a pail of water? If not, how does temperature differ from heat?

MATERIALS: Two measuring cups; three basins of water; ice; thermometer.

Add one fourth of a
cup of hot water to the
water in the basin.

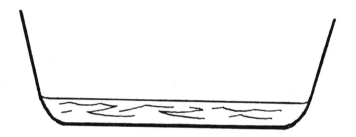

Add a full cup of
hot water to the
water in the basin.

Figure 15–1

METHOD: Part I — Place some ice into a basin of water; place lukewarm water into the second basin; into the third, place hot water. Put your left hand into the cold water and your right hand into the hot water and hold them there for about a minute. Now put both hands into the basin of lukewarm water at the same time. Are the reactions the same for each hand?

Part II — Place a cupful of water into each of two basins and record the temperature. Try to keep them as equal as possible. Using hot water from your kitchen faucet, fill one cup a quarter full and another cup completely full (Fig. 15–1). Add the contents of one cup to one basin and the contents of the other to the second basin. Mix and record the new temperature. Are they the same in each case? Why?

✂✂

DISCUSSION: The experiment in Part I demonstrates how unreliable our senses are in judging temperature. The hand that was placed into cold water and then into lukewarm water felt warm; the hand that was in hot water first and then in lukewarm water felt cool. Obviously, one's own temperature sense is unreliable. The hand that was first placed in cold water felt warm when it was placed into lukewarm water because heat traveled from the water *to the hand*. The hand that had been in hot water felt cold because heat traveled *from the hand* to the water. In other words, our senses detect the direction in which heat flows rather than the actual temperature.

You will also note that heat was said to travel to and from the hand; no reference was made to "cold."

Yet, it is evident that when you touch a piece of ice, "cold" travels from the ice to your hand; and if you are hardy enough to keep your hand on the ice, the ice melts. This makes it appear that "heat" is traveling to the ice. Which view is correct?

We must consider, once more, the meaning of temperature. It is the motion of molecules. Increasing the temperature increases the motion. In the wintertime, when the temperature drops below the freezing point of water, the ice gets colder. This means that these molecules are vibrating more slowly and that the molecules of water (ice) must have been vibrating even after they froze. Ice at 32° F. is "warm" compared to ice at 0° F.

The temperature of your hand is about 98.6° F. and, therefore, its molecules vibrate faster than those of ice. Upon touching the ice, your fast moving molecules collide with the slower moving ice molecules and speed them up. Their temperature increases and the ice melts. Since your own molecules have given part of their energy to the ice molecules, they slow down, which means they are at a lower temperature and you feel cold. We can state, therefore, that heat flows toward cold because the faster molecules bombard the slower molecules.

In Part II, we made the distinction between heat and temperature. We observed that a full cup of water and a quarter cup of water, both at the *same temperature,* caused a different temperature rise when added to equal amounts of water. The full cup caused a greater increase. How is this possible when equal temperatures in both cups indicate that their molecules vibrate at the same speeds?

Let us compare this to auto races at a track one mile long. We will assume that all the autos traveled at the same speed. Our measuring instrument, a stopwatch, tells us that it took

AMADEO AVOGADRO (1776-1856), Italian, is famous for the law which states that if different gases were placed in separate containers of the same size at the same temperature, they would contain the same number of molecules. Avogadro also investigated the way in which adding or removing heat from a substance affected its temperature. His experiments also included the study of the expansion of various substances when they were heated.

one minute for all the cars to travel one mile; that is, it measures their speed. But how many cars were in the race? A stopwatch cannot measure the number of cars.

The situation is similar to the measurement of temperature. The thermometer, which is bombarded by the moving molecules, can only measure the *speed* of the molecules. It cannot measure how many molecules are at that speed. In other words, the molecules in a cup of water at 100° F. are moving as fast as those in a quarter cup of water at the same temperature. The number of molecules vibrating tells us the total amount of energy or *heat* that is present. This is important because the more molecules we have at high temperatures, the more energy we can use. We can use the energy to melt ice, or heat a room, or for a thousand other purposes.

How do we measure the total heat available? First, we use a thermometer to tell us the temperature of the molecules. Second, we use *water* to tell us how many molecules are at that temperature.

A definite amount of heat is required to raise the temperature of one pound of water one degree Fahrenheit (1° F.). This amount of heat is called one British thermal unit or one B.T.U. This unit is used primarily in the United States and Great Britain to measure the heat given off by burning fuel, or the amount of heat removed by air conditioners. Scientists everywhere, including the United States and Great Britain, use *calories* to measure heat. Instead of a pound of water, a gram of water is used; there are 454 grams to a pound. Instead of Fahrenheit, the Centigrade scale is used. A calorie is the amount of heat that is required to raise the temperature of one gram of water one degree Centigrade. A large calorie or *kilocalorie* is the amount of heat it takes to raise the temperature of 1,000 grams of water (2.2 lbs.) one degree Centigrade. When books on nutrition use the word *calorie,* they mean large calorie. Therefore, when they say that a slice of bread is 65 calories, they mean that when it is completely burned in the body (or in the laboratory), it produces enough heat to increase the temperature of 1,000 grams of water by 65° C.

SELF-TEST
ANSWERS ON PAGE 175

1. Is one's own temperature sense a reliable judge of temperature?

2. Can our senses detect the direction in which heat flows?

3. What causes temperature?

4. Do molecules stop moving when water freezes?

5. What causes a cold object to become warmer when a warm object touches the colder object?

6. Is temperature the same as the total amount of heat a substance contains?

7. Does a thermometer measure the number of molecules there are at a certain temperature?

8. What is a British thermal unit?

9. What do scientists use as a measure of heat?

10. What is a calorie?

11. What is a large calorie or kilocalorie?

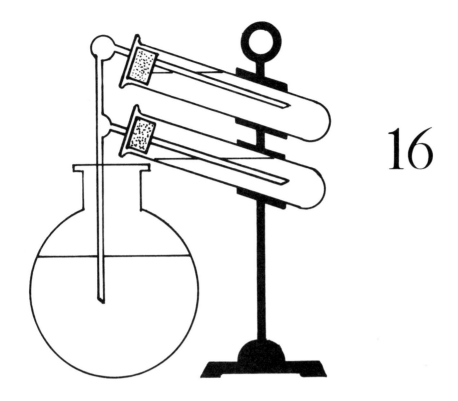

THE NATURE OF SOLUTIONS

What makes a hard, shiny, white substance such as table salt become invisible when mixed with water? We are aware, of course, that it really hasn't disappeared for it can be recovered by evaporation. To find the answer, let us examine the nature of solutions.

MATERIALS: Two lumps of table sugar; copper sulfate (blue crystals used to remove algae and other small plants from water); hypo (white sodium thiosulfate crystals, which look like table salt and are used in photography); water; 6 glasses; 2 spoons; saucepan; tissue paper; plate.

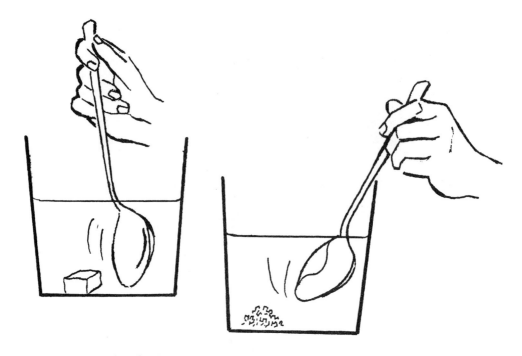

Stir both liquids (left with whole lump of sugar, right with crushed lump of sugar) at the same time.

Figure 16–1

METHOD: Part I — Select two lumps of table sugar. Place one in a glass and the other in a saucepan. With the aid of a spoon or a heavy object, crush the lump of sugar in the saucepan, then transfer it to the empty glass. This is done so that you have approximately equal weights of sugar in each glass. Add one half glass of water to each glass at the same time, and stir simultaneously (Fig. 16-1). In which glass does the sugar dissolve first? Why?

Part II — a) Select two crystals of copper sulfate (also known as blue vitriol), about the same size. A very important rule for chemists of ages nine to ninety to remember is — do not put chemicals into your mouth.

Half fill two glasses with water and drop one crystal into each glass. Cover one glass with a plate and stir the *other* mixture for about a minute. How do the colors compare in each glass? (Fig. 16–2) Examine the covered glass after an hour. Why does the copper sulfate seem to disobey the laws of gravity?

The copper sulfate seems to disobey the laws of gravity as it dissolves.

Why does stirring speed up solution?

Figure 16–2

b) Place a crystal of copper sulfate in a piece of tissue paper and hold it just under the surface of a glass of water (Fig. 16–3). Why does this crystal obey the laws of gravity whereas the crystal in a) did not?

Part III — Add several crystals of sugar to water. Stir until they dissolve. Keep adding sugar and stirring until no more dissolves. Place the glass in a saucepan of water and heat; this will warm the water in the glass evenly. Observe that the crystals that hadn't dissolved before, now dissolve. Continue to add sugar until no more dissolves. Remove from the heat and allow to cool. What happens to the solution?

Part IV — Add five teaspoonsful of hypo to a clean glass; then add a teaspoonful of water and stir. It will not all dissolve. Place the glass in a saucepan of water and heat. All of the hypo will dissolve in this very small amount of water. Remove

Figure 16–3

the glass and cover with a plate. Allow to cool and observe. Now add a very small crystal of hypo to this solution. Can you account for the sudden downpour of crystals? (Fig. 16–4)

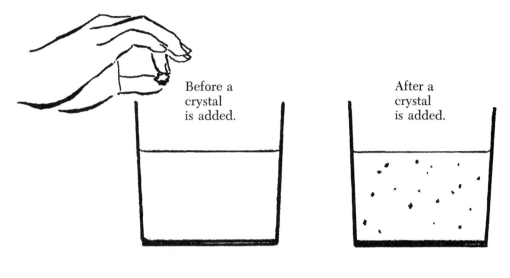

Before a
crystal
is added.

After a
crystal
is added.

Figure 16–4

DISCUSSION: Let us consider why a solid such as sugar or salt disappears when dissolved in water. We are aware that when lights are turned off in a room, and there is no stray light, we see nothing. We also know that when we light a match, our surroundings become visible. We can see a flame because it gives off its own light waves which travel to our eye and, through a series of events ending in our brain, we see the image. But why do we see the wall? Or a desk? Or a book? These objects give off no light of their own.

The light produced by a match or a bulb spreads in all directions. When it reaches a wall or a desk or any object, it bounces off — is reflected — to the eye and we see the object.

This occurs only if the atoms or molecules that make up the object are so close together that they stop the light and cause it to bounce back. We can compare this to a fence made up of vertical boards. If we throw a ball at the fence, the ball will bounce back straight or at an angle, depending on how it is thrown. If we separate the boards, so that the space between them is wider than the ball, the ball may go straight through; quite often, the ball hits a board and is "reflected." The farther apart the boards are, the more easily the ball is lost.

This explains why we cannot see air. The molecules that make up air are so far apart that light passes straight through without being reflected to the eye. This also applies to the invisible water vapor in the air. We can see water in its liquid form because the molecules are close to each other, although still quite far apart; most of the light passes through as was observed in the experiment on page 100.

Solid sugar can be seen because the molecules are so close together that most of the light is reflected to the eye. When sugar is placed in water, the water molecules separate the sugar molecules from each other and spread them evenly throughout the liquid. Since there is so much space between water molecules, the sugar molecules easily fit among them and still leave room for light waves to pass through. Because these waves are no longer reflected to the eye, they cannot be seen.

What is a solution? How does it differ from mud floating in water? We have already answered the question. In a solution, the particles are so small — of molecular size — and so far apart, that they do not reflect light. If a light beam is passed through water, it cannot be seen from the side. It must be faced squarely so that the light passing through the solution goes directly to the eye.

Particles of clay, though they may be very tiny, consist of clusters containing billions and billions of molecules which will reflect light. A beam of light passing through is clearly visible from the side owing to reflection from the individual

SVANTE AUGUST ARRHENIUS (1895-1927), Swedish physicist and chemist, originated the theory that certain substances separated into charged particles when placed into water, for which he was awarded the Nobel Prize in chemistry. He investigated the effects of poisons on living things, studied astronomy, and wrote articles on the origin of life and on the cause of the ice ages. He became director of the Nobel Institute of Physical Chemistry in 1905.

particles of clay. Therefore, this is not a solution. When a solution is well mixed, it is completely uniform throughout and will remain so, for dissolved particles will not settle.

In the instance we are discussing, a liquid — water — that does the dissolving is called the *solvent* and the dissolved substance — sugar — is called the *solute*. Though we cannot discuss them in detail here, there are many other types of solutions; there is steel, which is solid dissolved in solid; or liquid dissolved in liquid, such as alcohol and water; or gas in water, such as soda water; or gases in gases, such as air.

Solutions are often described on the basis of how much solute is dissolved as compared to solvent. When a small amount of solute is present — table salt, for example — in a large amount of solvent, such as water, we say that the solution is *dilute*. It is an inexact term but is useful and descriptive. (The word *many*, for instance, is not exact but is certainly quite useful in "many" situations.) When a large amount of solute is dissolved in a small amount of solvent, the solution is *concentrated*.

In Part I we observed that the crushed sugar dissolved more rapidly than the lump sugar. The reason is that the water must be able to reach the sugar before it can dissolve it. When the sugar is in one piece, the water can only dissolve the outside; the "inside" must wait until the outside is dissolved. When the sugar is crushed, the water can reach many "outsides" or surfaces at the same time and solution is speeded up.

In Part II a, it was evident that stirring hastened the solution of copper sulfate. As a substance dissolves, the solution immediately next to the substance becomes more concentrated and it becomes difficult for more to dissolve. When the solution is stirred, new liquid is constantly brought to the solute, thus hastening the process of solution.

A crystal of copper sulfate in water, even if it is not stirred, will slowly dissolve by itself. It appears to defy gravity as it *rises* and spreads through the liquid. This is a slow process and it may take several days for complete solution. The molecules of copper sulfate spread by a process called *diffusion*. As we noted in a previous section, molecules move at tremendous velocities. When a bottle of perfume is opened, it can be smelled several feet away because the rapidly moving molecules of perfume easily get through the wide spaces between the air molecules. In a similar manner, the particles of copper sulfate that were dissolved were set free and were able to move rapidly away; but the water molecules are closer together than molecules of air and cause the particles of copper sulfate to bounce back. In a few days, however, they all get through and spread evenly throughout the liquid.

In Part II b, the copper sulfate at the top dissolves slowly causing the solution to become heavy and sink. This enables new liquid to reach the copper sulfate and hastens the process of solution.

Experience shows that there is a limit to how much salt or sugar can be dissolved in a glass of water. This was demonstrated in Part III. Sugar was added until no more could be dissolved. At that point, the solution is said to be *saturated*. Upon heating, it was possible to dissolve more sugar until the solution became saturated again. Therefore, when we use the word "saturated," we must state at what temperature, for raising the temperature increases solubility. Conversely, lowering the temperature decreases solubility. There are, however, exceptions to this rule.

After the sugar solution cools to room temperature, the

sugar which had been dissolved at the higher temperature should come out of solution. Often it does; but very often, if it is cooled slowly, if the glass is clean, and if the liquid is not disturbed, the sugar will remain dissolved. Nobody is quite certain why! The solution is now said to be *supersaturated*. Addition of a small sugar crystal, called *seeding*, causes the excess sugar to come out of solution at once and fall to the bottom of the glass. Hypo was used in Part IV because a super-saturated solution is readily formed.

1. Why can't we see air?

2. Are the molecules of a solid usually further apart or closer together than those of a liquid?

3. Can water molecules separate sugar molecules from each other?

4. Why can't we see sugar molecules in solution?

5. If you pass a light beam through a solution, can you see it from the side?

6. Are particles of clay too small to reflect light?

7. Will a solution eventually settle upon standing?

8. What is a solvent? A solute?

9. What is a dilute solution?

10. What is a concentrated solution?

11. Which will dissolve more easily, a solid lump of sugar, or an equal weight of crushed sugar?

12. Does stirring hasten solution?

13. Will a substance such as sugar dissolve by itself if it is not stirred?

14. What is diffusion?

15. What is a saturated solution?

16. What is the effect of increasing temperature upon the solubility of sugar?

17. What is a supersaturated solution?

18. How do we seed a solution?

ROBERT BOYLE (1627-1691), English. One of his major contributions to science was his discovery concerning the behavior of gases. The law states that if the temperature of a gas is not allowed to change, the amount of space the gas occupies decreases in a uniform manner as pressure upon the gas is increased. Boyle was the first to understand the difference between an element and a compound. He also proved that sound travels through air.

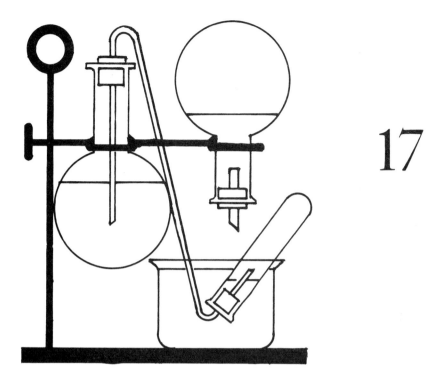

GASES AND WATER

Sea animals rely upon the solubility of gases in liquids for their survival. When water passes over the gills of a fish, dissolved oxygen is absorbed into the bloodstream.

What affects the solubility of gases? Is it temperature? Pressure? Does this type of solution behave in the same way as solutions of solids in liquids? Let us perform the following experiments to help determine the answers.

MATERIALS: Drinking glass; saucepan; water; bottle of soda; bottle opener.

METHOD: Part I — Fill a drinking glass with cold water and place it near a stove or where it can be warmed by the sun. Observe the gas bubbles that eventually form. What are they? Where do they form? (Fig. 17–1)

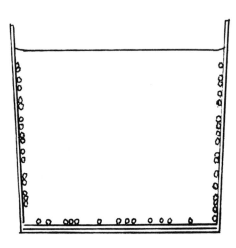

Bubbles of gas adhere to the sides of the container.

Figure 17–1

Part II — Boil some tap water in a saucepan. Cover it and allow to cool to room temperature without disturbing it. Taste the water. Now pour the water back and forth several times between two glasses (Fig. 17–2). Taste the water again. Is there a difference in taste? Why?

Part III — Examine the liquid in a soda bottle that has been standing unopened at room temperature. Do you see any bubbles of gas? Now open it quickly — over a sink! (Fig. 17–3) What does this tell you about the conditions under which a gas is soluble? This experiment demonstrates why accidents have been caused by exploding soda bottles and why they should never be stored near a stove or other warm place.

DISCUSSION: As the water in Part I becomes warmer, bubbles of gas appear and adhere to the sides of the glass (Fig. 17–1). When these bubbles become large enough, the forces of buoyancy overcome the forces of adhesion and the bubbles

Pour water several times from one glass to the other.

Figure 17–2

JOSEPH LOUIS GAY-LUSSAC (1778-1850), French, studied the composition of water, improved various industrial processes, and helped to discover methods of preparing the elements, boron and potassium. He is famous for the Law of Combining Volumes, which describes how the volumes of gases that combine during a chemical reaction are related to each other.

float to the top and escape. These two forces have been discussed in previous sections (see pages 29 and 81).

Figure 17–3

The bubbles of gas consisted of air that had been dissolved in water. Air is a mixture of several gases, but about 99 per cent of it is made of oxygen and nitrogen. Actually, the bubbles of gas that leave the water contain less oxygen than does the original air because oxygen is more soluble in water than nitrogen and more of it remains in solution.

The solubility of gases in liquids changes in a manner that is opposite to the way most solids behave. Numerous experiments by scientists have demonstrated that solids are usually (not always) more soluble in hot water. Part III of our experiment indicates that gases are *less* soluble in hot water; therefore, cooling water enables it to dissolve more gas.

We know that sugar dissolved in water makes it taste sweet, salt makes it taste salty, and vinegar makes it taste sour. If these dissolved substances add taste to water, should we expect air to do the same? The scientific answer is that we don't know. We have no reason to expect that a gas in water will behave like a liquid or solid. In fact, air behaved in an opposite manner with respect to solubility. We can make a clever guess, and we *should*, but many of the guesses made by our finest scientists have been proven wrong. We can expect air to affect the taste of water only if the experiment shows that it does. This may seem a minor and even obvious point, but it is the basis of modern scientific thought. In ancient times, this was not so. Logic, instead of experiment, was considered the best method of solving problems.

In Part II, after the boiled water had cooled to room temperature, we found that it had a peculiar, flat taste because the air had been boiled away — probably. This was confirmed when the water was poured from one container to another to allow air to dissolve. If this is done diligently, the water is restored to its original taste. If a fish had been placed in the boiled water after it had cooled, the fish would have drowned.

Pressure has almost no effect on the solubility of solids in water. It has a great effect on the solubility of gases in water. In Part III, no gas bubbles were observed in the unopened soda bottle despite the fact that the gas — carbon dioxide — was less soluble in the warmer liquid. Upon removing the cap, thereby decreasing the pressure, the gas suddenly and forcibly came out of solution, causing the liquid to overflow.

The danger of keeping a closed bottle of soda near a stove

is that the gas becomes less soluble and tries to leave the liquid. However, the cap is on tight and the increased pressure within the bottle keeps it soluble. But as heat increases, the gas becomes even less soluble; the tremendously increased pressure causes the bottle to break. This results in a sudden reduction

GAY-LUSSAC and BIOT making their balloon ascent for scientific observations in 1804.

in pressure allowing more gas to come out of solution all at once, and the liquid and broken glass fly in all directions.

Another example of the effect of dissolved gases can be observed when a deep-sea diver descends into the water. Air is forced into his diving suit to prevent the weight of the water from crushing him. The air enters his lungs and dissolves in his blood — at increased pressure. If he were to be pulled up quickly, it would be the same as if the cap from a soda bottle were removed. Decreased pressure causes the air in his lungs to expand and decreases the solubility of air in his blood. The air would come out of solution in the form of gas bubbles throughout the blood vessels of his body, causing damage and pain in the joints and muscles. This is called the "bends."

Since oxygen is more soluble than nitrogen, these bubbles consist mostly of the latter. Quite often, the gas that is fed to the diver contains oxygen mixed with helium instead of nitrogen. Helium is less soluble in blood and there is less likelihood of large bubbles of gas forming during the ascent of the diver.

SELF-TEST
ANSWERS ON PAGE 176

1. As water becomes warmer, bubbles of gas appear. What are these bubbles?

2. In which are gases more soluble, hot water or cold water?

3. Does air dissolved in water have an effect upon its taste?

4. Is it possible for a fish to drown in water?

5. What effect does increased pressure have upon the solubility of gases in water?

6. A closed bottle of soda may explode when stored in a warm place. What causes this?

7. As a diver descends into water, does the amount of air dissolved in his blood increase or decrease?

8. As a diver rises in water, dissolved gases tend to come out of his blood. What does most of this gas consist of?

9. What has replaced nitrogen in the gas that is fed to divers, because it is less soluble in blood?

ANTOINE L. LAVOISIER (1743-1794), French, is known as the father of modern chemistry. He was the first to understand the true nature of burning. His precise methods led him to the conclusion that burning was a combination of the oxygen of the air with another substance. Lavoisier studied respiration and body heat in living things, and conducted experiments to determine the composition of water and various organic compounds.

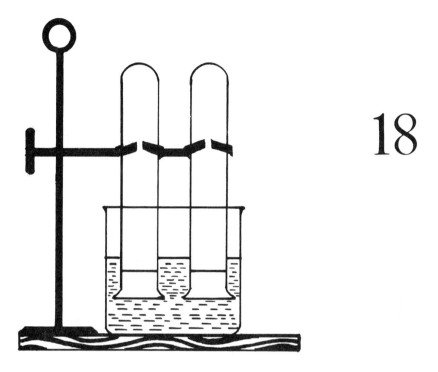

THE ELECTROLYSIS OF WATER

The formula for water is H_2O. This is a simplfied way of stating that one molecule of water consists of two atoms of hydrogen and one atom of oxygen. But hydrogen and oxygen are gases! Oxygen is an aid to burning, and hydrogen is so flammable that it is no longer used in dirigibles; yet water is

Remove one inch of protective covering (insulation) from the ends of five béll wires with the aid of a knife.

Figure 18-1a

used to put out fires. Does water really consist of hydrogen and oxygen?

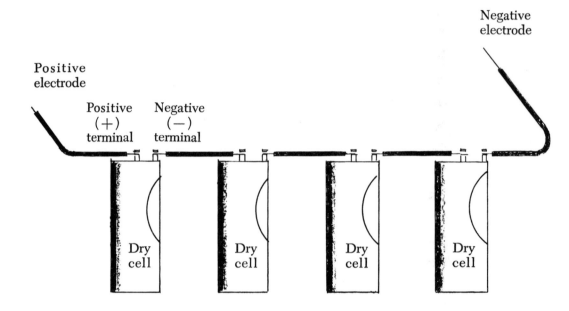

Connect the end of one wire to the center (positive or +) terminal of a dry cell. Connect the other end of the wire to the negative (or −) terminal at the edge of another dry cell. Continue until all the cells are connected. The bare end of the wire extending from the center of the dry cell is called the positive electrode and the end of the other wire is the negative electrode.

Figure 18–1b

MATERIALS: Washing soda (sodium carbonate); water; basin; two juice glasses; four #6 dry cells (batteries); three bell wires, one foot long; two bell wires, two feet long; toothpick.

METHOD: Part I — Dissolve four teaspoonsful of washing soda in a small basin of water. Place two juice glasses into the water on their sides. Add sufficient water to cover the glasses, and set them bottoms up. The solution will remain in the glasses. Connect the dry cells as illustrated in Figure 18–1a, b, and c.

Place the electrodes into the glasses while they are submerged. A stream of bubbles will begin to rise from each electrode. As the gas forms, it forces the water out of the glasses. Is the rate of gas formation equal in both glasses?

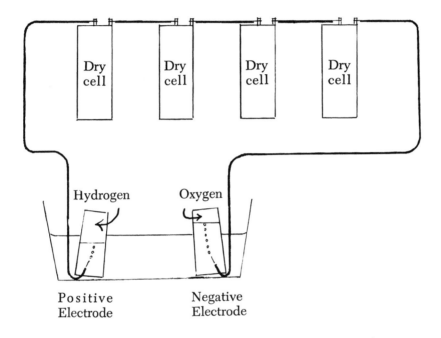

Figure 18–1c

Part II — When one of the glasses is completely filled with gas, remove it and place it bottom up on a smooth surface so that the gas does not escape. Ignite a wooden toothpick, then lift the glass straight up; hold the mouth away from you — this is important — and ignite the gas (Fig. 18–2a). You will hear a slight "pop."

Figure 18–2a

Part III — When the second glass is filled with gas, ignite a wooden toothpick, then lift the glass. Blow out the flame so that all you have is a glowing ember. Insert this into the glass. How does this reaction differ from that in Part III? (Fig. 18–2b)

DISCUSSION: Pure water is a very poor conductor of electricity. In order to help current flow, washing soda is added. Substances that are used for this purpose are called *electrolytes*.

The electric current separates the water molecules into

the two elements of which they are composed. This process is called *electrolysis*. The hydrogen is released as a gas at the negative electrode, and the oxygen is released at the positive electrode.

Figure 18–2b

The glass containing hydrogen fills more than twice as fast as the glass containing oxygen. The rate should be exactly two to one; however, some oxygen is lost because it is more soluble than hydrogen. We "proved" hydrogen was present by igniting it and observing the "pop." This is not a conclusive test for hydrogen, as is often claimed. Any fast burning gas will "pop" and burn with a blue color — for example, burning natural gas in a stove. A complete identification is beyond the scope of this book. Experiments by skilled scientists have proven that hydrogen gas is produced in this process. We also "proved" that oxygen is present when the glowing wood burst into flame. However, there are other gases that will perform in a similar manner.

It was observed that the hydrogen and oxygen gas did not behave as they do when they are part of a molecule of water. The hydrogen burned and the oxygen supported combustion. It has been established again and again that elements lose their original properties when they unite to become a compound.

This experiment also indicates that each molecule of water contains twice as much hydrogen as oxygen since they were produced in that ratio when the electric current destroyed the molecule. Therefore, it is quite natural to say that a molecule of water is H_2O. *But,* why can't it be a molecule consisting of four hydrogen atoms and two oxygen atoms? This would also produce twice as much hydrogen as oxygen. Scientists now believe that water molecules may travel in pairs, or triplets, or quadruplets, and research is still going on in this area.

1. What is the chemical formula for water?

2. Is pure water a good conductor of electricity?

3. Washing soda in water aids the flow of electricity. What is this type of substance called?

4. What is electrolysis?

5. Compare the amounts of hydrogen and oxygen formed during electrolysis.

6. In this experiment, what was the test for hydrogen?

7. What was the test for oxygen?

8. What does the symbol H_2O mean?

JOSEPH PRIESTLEY (1733-1804), English, while practicing as a clergyman, conducted experiments in chemistry and electricity. He discovered oxygen, but did not realize the exact nature of the gas. He also discovered other gases including carbon dioxide, nitrogen, and ammonia, and was in contact with such men as Benjamin Franklin, Thomas Jefferson, and George Washington.

HOW TO MAKE YOUR OWN BALANCE

A simple and very useful balance can be constructed as illustrated in Figure 19a. All parts of the balance except the

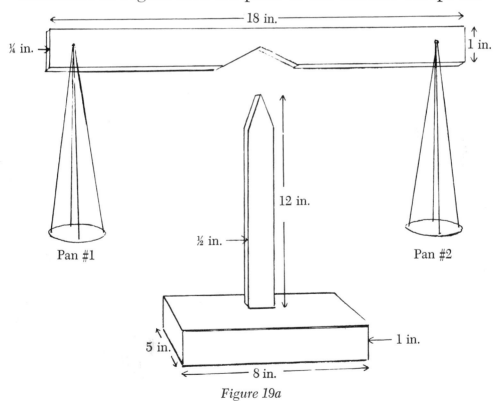

18 in.

¼ in.

1 in.

12 in.

½ in.

Pan #1

Pan #2

5 in.

1 in.

8 in.

Figure 19a

pans are made of wood. The pans are the tops of old tin cans and may be cut so that they balance each other. Tie heavy thread through four holes spaced evenly around each pan (Fig. 19b).

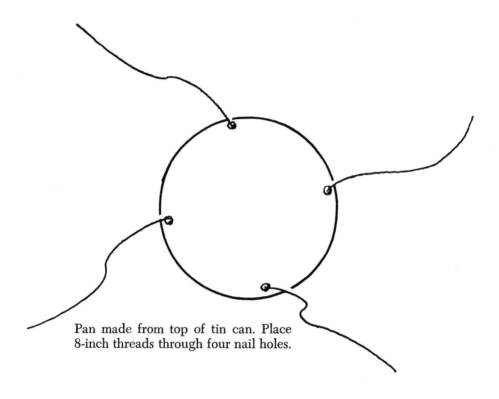

Pan made from top of tin can. Place 8-inch threads through four nail holes.

Figure 19b

Use coins as weights. A dime weighs approximately 2.5 grams (there are about 28.4 grams in an ounce); a nickel weighs five grams. You can use combinations of coins to give you additional weights; for instance, two nickels weigh ten grams. You can also make smaller weights by placing a nickel on pan No. 1 at the left and balancing it with nails placed on pan No. 2.

Let us assume that five nails will balance one nickel. Since

168

a nickel weighs five grams, each nail weighs one gram and can be used as a one gram weight.

In order to weigh an object, place it on pan No. 1. Add weights to pan No. 2 until a balance is achieved (Fig. 19c). De-

(The Bettman Archive, Inc.)

GALILEO making his experiments on the velocity of falling bodies, from the leaning Tower of Pisa. "They were seen to fall evenly."

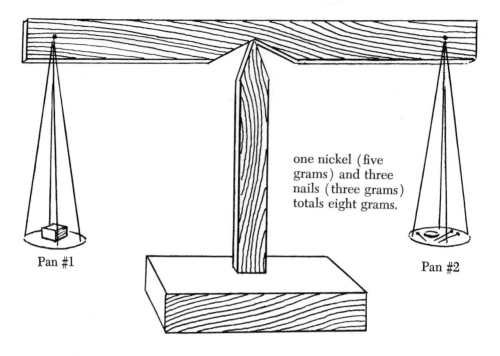

one nickel (five grams) and three nails (three grams) totals eight grams.

Pan #1

Pan #2

Weighing a small block of wood

Figure 19c

termine the weight of the object by adding together the weights of all the items on pan No. 2. Thus, if there is one nickel (five grams) and three nails (three grams) the object weighs eight grams.

ANSWERS TO SELF-TESTS

1 IS WATER REALLY HEAVY?

1. The weight of the water.   2. At the topmost opening.   3. The lowest opening.   4. The height of the water above the opening. 5. Water pressure was caused by the weight of the water.   6. His eardrums.

2 HOW DOES WATER MULTIPLY PRESSURE?

1. Blaise Pascal.   2. No.   3. It spreads equally throughout the water.   4. The water pressure increases.   5. The height and weight of the water.   6. An air pump forces air against the oil. The pressure at the surface of the oil is transmitted throughout the oil.   7. The upward pressure of the water beneath your hand is slightly greater than the pressure on top of your hand.

3 HOW DOES A STEEL SHIP FLOAT?

1. It is the upward force of water upon an object.   2. Archimedes.
3. The can will sink deeper into the water.   4. No. It will sink deeper
in tap water.   5. Pebbles.   6. An object will float if it can displace an
amount of water equal to its own weight.   7. They are equal to each
other.   8. A stone sinks because the weight of the water it displaces is
less than the weight of the stone.   9. They are equal.   10. Almost
sixty-two and one half pounds.   11. A quart of salt water weighs more
than a quart of tap water; or salt water weighs more than an equal
volume of tap water.

4 LET'S PROVE IT

1. Proof, usually through accurate measurements.   2. The water
level rises.   3. This was demonstrated by weighing the amount of
water displaced.   4. The volume of water displaced is less than the
weight of the ring.   5. It is a statement that describes how something
will behave, and for which no exception has been found.   6. When
weighing equal volumes of metals, they are found to have different
weights. The weight of each metal compared to the amount of space it
takes up is called its density.   7. The loss of weight is due to the upward pressure of water upon the metal (buoyancy).   8. The weight of
metal in air compared to its loss in weight in water.   9. Yes. Each
metal has its own specific gravity.

5 THE CARTESIAN DIVER, or WHAT MAKES A SUBMARINE
   RISE AND FALL?

1. It is a toy that can change its buoyancy in water. In this experiment, it is a vial floating mouth downward in a jar of water.   2. René
Descartes.   3. The Cartesian Diver sinks.   4. The Cartesian Diver
rises.   5. As often as you wish.   6. The law of buoyancy.   7. By
pressing the rubber membrane.   8. The additional weight of the water
causes the vial to sink.   9. It is compressed by the water.   10. The

compressed air forces water out of the vial and it rises.   11. Water is admitted to it tanks.

6   WHY DOES OIL FLOAT?

1. Water.   2. Water will cause the fire to spread.   3. Water.   4. The water and carbon tetrachloride separate and the water floats on the carbon tetrachloride.   5. The oil and water separate and the oil floats on the water.   6. The Carbona is heavier than the water.   7. A quart of milk weighs slightly more.   8. The comparison of the weight of a volume of liquid to an equal volume of water.   9. The specific gravity of oil is less than that of water.   10. Sand, table salt, baking soda, damp towel.   11. Alcohol.   12. Alcohol dissolves in water.

7   CAN A NEEDLE FLOAT?

1. Molecules.   2. Cohesion.   3. Surface tension.   4. No.   5. No.   6. The attraction between water molecules forms an invisible film.   7. Soap is added; the needle may also be nudged with a toothpick.   8. It weakened the attraction of water molecules for each other. 9. The dirt must be attracted to the water molecules.   10. Yes.   11. The water and soap are then attracted to the dirt and wash it away.

8   WATER AND SURFACE TENSION

1. Two.   2. The two layers disappeared and formed a cloudy mixture.   3. Small drops of water form.   4. The attraction of water molecules for themselves is greater than their attraction for oil.   5. Its molecules are not attracted to oil.   6. Yes.   7. Part of the soap molecule breaks the oil into tiny drops and surrounds each drop.   8. Part of the soap molecule is attracted to water.   9. An emulsion.   10. No. 11. Homogenized milk; mayonnaise.   12. Egg yolk.   13. Milk is forced through tiny holes in order to break the butterfat into tiny droplets.   14. The soap lowered the surface tension at the rear, whereas the

surface tension at the front remained the same.   15. The sticks moved apart.   16. The surface tension between them was lowered by the soap or alcohol.   17. Water wets (attracts) both of them.   18. Water was no longer attracted to your finger, whereas water attracted the pepper.

9   SOAP BUBBLES

1. The weight of the liquid is small compared to the strength of the film.   2. Glycerine.   3. Smaller.   4. Yes.   5. The surface tension of a soap solution is greater than that of water.

10   ADHESION AND CAPILLARY ACTION

1. The attraction between different types of molecules.   2. Yes. 3. Adhesion.   4. No.   5. Adhesion makes it difficult to separate the water from the glass and cohesion makes it difficult to separate the layer of water between the glass plates.   6. A narrow tube causes a liquid to rise.   7. Eventually, the weight of the water column becomes equal to the force of adhesion.   8. A narrow column, since it weighs less.   9. No. It moves downward because its own cohesive forces are greater than the adhesive forces between itself and the glass.

11   PERPETUAL MOTION—AT LAST?

1. A system remaining forever in motion without outside help.   2 Loss of energy due to friction.   3. Yes.   4. The loss of heat caused by the small amount of friction between the water and the glass and between water and water will cause the water to freeze.   5. The warmer air surrounding the tube will warm the water and restore lost energy.

12   WATER AND LIGHT

1. It enables us to do work.   2. Particles or waves.   3. Approximately 186,000 miles per second.   4. Light travels more slowly in water than in air.   5. Yes.   6. In a straight line.   7. It changes direc-

tion.   8. It increases.   9. It is the bending of light when it passes from one material, such as air, to another, such as water.   10. Reflection. 11. Critical angle.   12. No.   13. The difference in the speed of light in air and in water.   14. Because of refraction.   15. You are looking upward at an angle greater than the critical angle.   16. Its curved surface increases the bending or refraction of light.   17. Because of reflection from the edges of the stream when the light tries to pass through at an angle greater than the critical angle.   18. Refraction.

13   WATER, LIGHT, AND COLOR
1. A glass triangle used to study light.   2. The spectrum.   3. The separation of light into its different colors.   4. A mixture of colors. 5. They are the same.   6. The distance from the crest of one wave to that of another.   7. As separate colors. 8. No.   9. Violet.   10. By dispersing light.

14   DOES HOT WATER WEIGH THE SAME AS COLD WATER?
1. Weigh equal volumes.   2. Cold water weighs more than an equal volume of hot water.   3. Yes.   4. Movement of water caused by differences in its temperature.   5. Winds, convection currents, earthquakes, tides, rotation of the earth.   6. Water expands upon heating and less of it can therefore fit into a quart bottle.   7. It freezes and boils rather easily.   8. The energy of the molecules as they move. 9. It expands upon freezing and becomes less dense.   10. 0°C. (32°F.).   11. There is more space between its molecules.

15   IS THERE A DIFFERENCE BETWEEN TEMPERATURE AND HEAT?
1. No.   2. Yes.   3. The motion of molecules.   4. No.   5. The fast moving molecules of the warmer object bombard the slower moving molecules of the cold object.   6. No.   7. No.   8. The amount of

heat that will raise the temperature of one pound of water 1°F. 9. Calories.   10. The amount of heat necessary to raise one gram of water 1°C.   11. One thousand small calories.

16   THE NATURE OF SOLUTIONS

1. Its molecules are too far apart and do not reflect light.   2. Closer together.   3. Yes.   4. They are too far apart.   5. No.   6. No. 7. No.   8. A solvent is something that dissolves a substance. The dissolved substance is called a solute.   9. A small amount of solute dissolved in a large amount of solvent.   10. A large amount of solute dissolved in a small amount of solvent.   11. An equal weight of crushed sugar.   12. Yes.   13. Yes.   14. The movement of molecules so that they spread out.   15. A solution in which no more solute can be dissolved.   16. The solubility is increased.   17. A solution that contains more solute than it can ordinarily hold at that temperature. 18. Excess crystals will come out of a supersaturated solution when a small crystal of that substance is added.

17   GASES AND WATER

1. Air that has been dissolved.   2. Cold water.   3. Yes.   4. Yes. 5. Increases the solubility.   6. The decreased solubility of the gas in warm liquid causes it to come out of solution, increasing the pressure. 7. Increases.   8. Nitrogen.   9. Helium.

18   THE ELECTROLYSIS OF WATER

1. H_2O. 2. No. 3. Electrolyte. 4. The destruction of molecules by electricity.   5. Twice as much hydrogen forms as oxygen, when measured by volume (the amount of space each gas takes up).   6. When it is ignited, it will "pop."   7. A glowing toothpick bursts into flame when placed in the glass containing oxygen.   8. One molecule of water contains two atoms of hydrogen and one atom of oxygen.

TABLE OF MEASUREMENTS

ENGLISH UNITS

Linear Measure

1 foot (ft.) = 12 inches (in.)
3 feet = 1 yard (yd.)
5,280 feet = 1 statute or land mile (mi.)

Area Measure

1 square foot (sq. ft.) = 144 square inches (sq. in.)
9 square feet = 1 square yard (sq. yd.)
9 square feet = 1,296 square inches

Liquid Measure

4 gills (gi.) = 1 pint (pt.)
2 pints = 1 quart (qt.)
4 quarts = 1 gallon (gal.)
8 pints = 1 gallon

Weight

1 pound (lb.) = 16 ounces (oz.)
1 ton (tn.) = 2,000 pounds

METRIC UNITS*

Linear Measure

1 meter (m.) = 100 centimeters (cm.)
1 meter = 1,000 millimeters (mm.)
1 centimeter = 10 millimeters

Area Measure

1 square centimeter = 100 square millimeters
1 square meter = 1 million square millimeters

Volume Measure

1 liter (l.) = 1,000 milliliters (ml.)

Weight

1 kilogram (kg.) = 1,000 grams (gm.)
1 gram = 1,000 milligrams (mg.)
1 metric ton (t.) = 1,000 kilograms

TABLE OF COMPARATIVE WEIGHTS AND MEASURES

English	Metric
1 inch =	2.54 centimeters
1 yard =	0.9144 meters
1 quart =	0.946 liters
1 ounce =	28.35 grams
1 pound =	453.6 grams
1 ton =	0.907 metric tons

Metric	English
1 centimeter =	0.394 inches
1 meter =	1.094 yards (39.37 inches)
1 liter =	1.06 quarts
1 gram =	0.035 ounces
1 kilogram =	2.2 pounds
1 metric ton =	1.10 tons

* Used by most scientists

APPARATUS FOUND
IN PRESENT-DAY LABORATORY

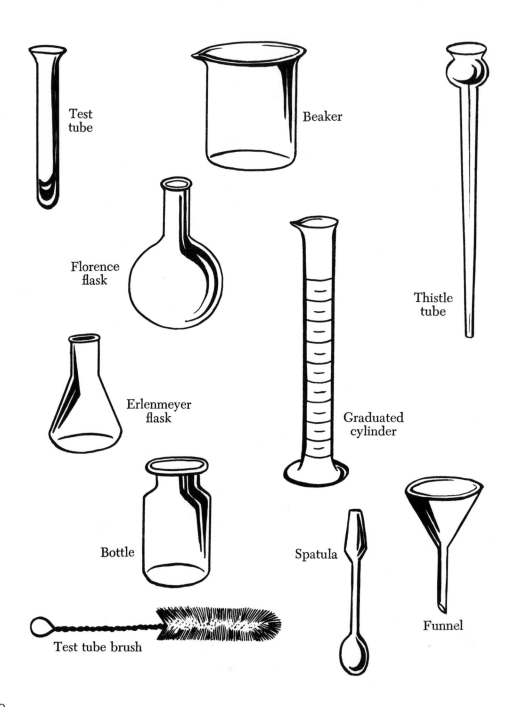

Test tube

Beaker

Thistle tube

Florence flask

Erlenmeyer flask

Graduated cylinder

Bottle

Spatula

Funnel

Test tube brush

Ring stand and ring

Wing top

Bunsen burner

Forceps

Test tube clamp

Wire gauze

Crucible and its cover

Evaporating dish

Iron clamp

Crucible tongs

Triangular file

Mortar and pestle

Watch glass

CHEMICAL ELEMENTS OF THE UNIVERSE

Element	Symbol	Discoverer
Actinium	Ac	Debierne (1899)
Aluminum	Al	Oersted (1825)
Americium	Am	Seaborg (1944)
Antimony	Sb	Valentine (1450)
Argon	Ar	Rayleigh, Ramsay (1894)
Arsenic	As	Magnus (13th C.)
Astatine	At	Corson (1940)
Barium	Ba	Davy (1808)
Berkelium	Bk	Thompson, Ghiorso, Seaborg (1949)
Beryllium	Be	Vauquelin (1798)
Bismuth	Bi	Valentine (15th C.)
Boron	B	Davy (1808)
Bromine	Br	Balard (1826)
Cadmium	Cd	Stromeyer (1817)
Calcium	Ca	Davy (1808)
Californium	Cf	Thompson (1950)
Carbon	C	(Ancient)
Cerium	Ce	Klaproth (1803)
Cesium	Cs	Bunsen, Kirchoff (1861)
Chlorine	Cl	Scheele (1774)
Chromium	Cr	Vauquelin (1797)
Cobalt	Co	Brandt (1735)
Copper	Cu	(Ancient)
Curium	Cm	Seaborg (1944)
Dysprosium	Dy	Boisbaudran (1886)
Einsteinium	E	Ghiorso (1952)
Erbium	Er	Mosander (1843)
Europium	Eu	Demarcay (1901)
Fermium	Fm	Ghiorso (1953)
Fluorine	F	Scheele (1771)
Francium	Fr	Perey (1939)
Gadolinium	Gd	Marignac (1886)
Gallium	Ga	Boisbaudran (1875)
Germanium	Ge	Winkler (1886)

Gold	Au	(Ancient)
Hafnium	Hf	Coster, Hevesy (1923)
Helium	He	Ramsay (1895)
Holmium	Ho	Cleve (1879)
Hydrogen	H	Cavendish (1766)
Indium	In	Reich, Richter (1863)
Iodine	I	Courtois (1811)
Iridium	Ir	Tennant (1804)
Iron	Fe	(Ancient)
Krypton	Kr	Ramsay, Travers (1898)
Lanthanum	La	Mosander (1839)
Lawrencium	Lw	Ghiorso, Sikkeland, Larsh, Latimer (1961)
Lead	Pb	(Ancient)
Lithium	Li	Arfvedson (1817)
Lutetium	Lu	Welsbach, Urbain (1907)
Magnesium	Mg	Liebig, Bussy (1830)
Manganese	Mn	Gahn (1774)
Mendelevium	Mv	Ghiorso (1955)
Mercury	Hg	(Ancient)
Molybdenum	Mo	Hjelm (1782)
Neodymium	Nd	Welsbach (1885)
Neon	Ne	Ramsay, Travers (1898)
Neptunium	Np	McMillan & Abelson (1940)
Nickel	Ni	Cronstedt (1751)
Niobium (Form. Columbium)	Nb	Hatchett (1801)
Nitrogen	N	Rutherford (1772)
Nobelium	No	Ghiorso (1957)
Osmium	Os	Tennant (1804)
Oxygen	O	Priestley, Scheele (1774)
Palladium	Pd	Wollaston (1803)
Phosphorus	P	Brandt (1669)
Platinum	Pt	Ulloa (1735)
Plutonium	Pu	Seaborg (1940)
Polonium	Po	P. & M. Curie (1898)
Potassium	K	Davy (1807)
Praseodymium	Pr	Welsbach (1885)
Promethium	Pm	Glendenin & Marinsky (1945)
Protactinium	Pa	Hahn & Meitner (1917)

Radium	Ra	P. & M. Curie, Bemont (1898)
Radon	Rn	Dorn (1900)
Rhenium	Re	Noddack & Tacke (1925)
Rhodium	Rh	Wollaston (1803)
Rubidium	Rb	Bunsen, Kirchoff (1861)
Ruthenium	Ru	Claus (1845)
Samarium	Sm	Boisbaudran (1879)
Scandium	Sc	Nilson (1879)
Selenium	Se	Berzelius (1817)
Silicon	Si	Berzelius (1823)
Silver	Ag	(Ancient)
Sodium	Na	Davy (1807)
Strontium	Sr	Crawford (1790)
Sulfur	S	(Ancient)
Tantalum	Ta	Eckeberg (1802)
Technetium	Tc	Perrier & Segre (1937)
Tellurium	Te	Von Reichenstein (1782)
Terbium	Tb	Mosander (1843)
Thallium	Tl	Crookes (1861)
Thorium	Th	Berzelius (1828)
Thulium	Tm	Cleve (1879)
Tin	Sn	(Ancient)
Titanium	Ti	Gregor (1789)
Tungsten (Alternate Wolfram)	W	d'Elhujar (1783)
Uranium	U	Klaproth (1789)
Vanadium	V	Sefstrom (1830)
Xenon	Xe	Ramsay, Travers (1898)
Ytterbium	Yb	Marignac (1878)
Yttrium	Y	Gadolin (1794)
Zinc	Zn	(Ancient)
Zirconium	Zr	Klaproth (1789)

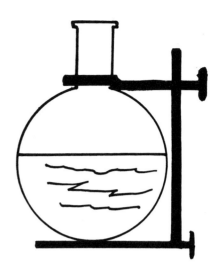

GLOSSARY

adhesion—the attraction between different types of molecules, as between water and glass.

Archimedes—a Greek scientist who studied the effects of buoyancy in 250 B.C.

atom—the smallest part of an element that can exist and still be that element. Examples of elements are oxygen, hydrogen, carbon.

British thermal unit (B.T.U.)—the amount of heat required to raise the temperature of one pound of water one degree Fahrenheit.

buoyancy—the upward force exerted upon an object in a liquid or gas.

calorie—the amount of heat required to raise the temperature of one gram of water one degree Centigrade.

capillary action—the rising or depression of a liquid in a capillary tube.

capillary tube—a tube with a very narrow opening.

carbon tetrachloride—a colorless liquid used for cleaning, and to extinguish fires.

Cartesian Diver—a toy whose buoyancy can be increased or decreased while it is in water.

cohesion—attraction between the molecules of a single substance, such as the attraction of water molecules for each other.

compound—a substance, such as water or table salt, made of two or more kinds of atoms which have combined so as to lose their original properties.

concentrated solution—a large amount of substance dissolved in a small amount of solvent.

convection current—the flow of liquid or gas caused by differences in temperature.

copper sulfate—blue vitriol; blue crystals; a very small amount is used to kill small plants in water.

critical angle—the angle at which a light wave, passing upward through water, is totally reflected downward.

density—the weight of a substance compared to the amount of space it occupies.

diffusion—rapid-moving molecules spread out in all directions, as when the molecules of perfume spread through the air.

dilute solution—a small amount of substance dissolved in a large amount of solvent.

dispersion—the separation of light into its various colors as when raindrops separate sunlight to form a rainbow.

electrolysis—the use of electricity to decompose a substance.

electrolyte—a substance such as washing soda or table salt, that is added to water in order to help it conduct electric current.

element—a substance made of only one kind of atom. There are 103 elements, and various combinations of these make up every substance in the universe.

emulsion—liquids which do not dissolve in each other, such as oil and water, are made to form a mixture. When one of these is broken into tiny droplets it will often remain suspended throughout the other liquid. An example is homogenized milk which consists of minute droplets of fat suspended throughout the remainder of the liquid.

glycerin—a colorless, odorless, sticky liquid that resembles water in appearance. It is used in the manufacture of cosmetics and medicines.

gram—a unit of weight in the metric system. There are approximately 28.4 grams to an ounce.

hypo—(sodium thiosulfate) white crystals which look like table salt; they are used in photography.

insulator—a substance that prevents the flow of electricity; a substance that prevents the flow of heat.

law—a general statement of facts that have been observed always to hold true.

mercury—a heavy, silvery liquid metal; it is often used to make thermometers.

molecule—the smallest part of a substance, such as water or sugar, that can exist and still be the same substance. If a molecule is broken down further it changes to its individual elements.

Pascal's law—the pressure upon a liquid at any point is spread equally throughout the liquid.

perpetual motion machine—a machine that will work forever without outside help because there is no loss of energy due to friction.

prism—a piece of glass shaped like a triangle.

rainbow—an array of colors formed when the different light waves of sunlight or other white light are separated from each other by means of raindrops, prisms, or any other means.

refraction—the bending of light when it passes from one medium, such as water, to another medium, such as air.

reflection—the return of light waves from a surface.

saturated solution—a solution that contains the maximum amount of dissolved substance.

soluble—the ability of a substance to dissolve in another substance, as sugar dissolves in water.

solute—a dissolved substance. In a sugar solution, for example, sugar is the solute.

solvent—a substance that dissolves another substance; water is a solvent for sugar.

specific gravity—the density of a substance as compared to the density of water. Since the density of water is considered to be *one*, a substance having a specific gravity greater than one is denser than water and a substance having a specific gravity less than one is less dense than water.

spectrum—an array of rainbow colors and invisible waves such as X-rays, radio waves, and ultra-violet waves caused by the breaking up of light into the waves of which it is composed.

supersaturated solution—a solution that contains more dissolved substance than it can ordinarily hold.

surface tension—attraction between the molecules at the surface of a liquid causing it to behave as if there were an invisible film.

temperature—a measure of the intensity of heat or of how hot or cold an object is.

thermometer—a device used to measure the temperature of an object or a space. It may depend upon a liquid, such as mercury or alcohol, a solid, or a gas, which expands when heated and contracts when cooled.

volume—the amount of space occupied by a substance.

wavelength—the distance from the crest of one wave to the crest of another.

weight—the force that gravity exerts upon an object; it is the measure of the earth's attraction for that object. This force of attraction varies with the size of the earth, moon, sun, or other planets; therefore, an object will have a different weight on other bodies in space.

water level—the height of the surface of a body of water.

water pressure—the weight of water pressing down at a particular point.

BIBLIOGRAPHY

THE CAVENDISH LABORATORY by Egon Larsen (*Franklin Watts, Inc., New York, 1962*)

CRYSTALS by Raymond A. Wohlrabe (*J. B. Lippincott Co., New York, 1962*)

DISCOVERING CHEMISTRY by Elizabeth K. Cooper (*Harcourt, Brace & Co., New York, 1959*)

ELEMENTS OF THE UNIVERSE by Glenn T. Seaborg & Evans G. Valens (*E. P. Dutton & Co., Inc., 1958*)

EXPERIMENTS FOR YOUNG CHEMISTS by E. H. Coulson & A.E.J. Trinder (*G. Bell & Sons, Ltd., London, 1963*)

EXPERIMENTS IN CHEMISTRY by Nelson Beeler & Franklyn Branley (*Thomas Y. Crowell Company, New York, 1952*)

INSIDE THE ATOM by Isaac Asimov (*Abelard-Schuman, Ltd., New York, 1961*)

THE MAGIC OF ELECTRICITY by Sam Rosenfeld (*Lothrop, Lee & Shepard, New York, 1963*)

MEN OF SCIENCE AND INVENTION (*American Heritage Publishing Co., New York, 1960*)

101 Science Projects by George K. Stone (*Prentice-Hall, Inc., New Jersey, 1963*)

Physics for Everybody by Germaine & Arthur Beiser (*E. P. Dutton & Co., Inc., 1956*)

Science and Discovery (*International Graphic Society, Englewood Cliffs, New Jersey, 1960*)

Science, Science, Science by Russell Hamilton (*Franklin Watts, Inc., New York, 1960*)

The Second Book of Experiments by Leonard de Vries (*The Macmillan Co., New York, 1963*)

Simple Chemical Experiments by A. P. Morgan (*Appleton, New York, 1954*)

There's Adventure in Chemistry by Julian May (*Popular Mechanics Press, Chicago, 1957*)

Understanding Light by Beulah Tannenbaum & Myra Stillman (*Whittlesey House, New York, 1960*)

Water: Miracle of Nature by Thomson King (*Collier Books, New York, 1953*)

The Wonder of Light by Hy Ruchlis (*Harper & Bros., New York, 1960*)

Young People's Book of Science by G. O. Blough (*McGraw-Hill, New York, 1958*)

INDEX

Figures in *Italics* Indicate Illustrations